GRADE 2

California Treasures

Practice Book

S0-AJX-952

Macmillan/McGraw-Hill

B

The McGraw·Hill Companies

 Macmillan
McGraw-Hill

Published by Macmillan/McGraw-Hill, of McGraw-Hill Education, a division of The McGraw-Hill Companies, Inc., Two Penn Plaza, New York, New York 10121.

Copyright © by Macmillan/McGraw-Hill. All rights reserved. No part of this publication may be reproduced or distributed in any form or by any means, or stored in a database or retrieval system, without the prior written consent of The McGraw-Hill Companies, Inc., including, but not limited to, network storage or transmission, or broadcast for distance learning.

Printed in the United States of America

15 QTN 16

Contents

Unit I • Friends and Family

Contents

Unit 2 • Community Heroes

© Macmillan/McGraw-Hill

Contents

Unit 3 • Let's Create

© Macmillan/McGraw-Hill

Contents

Unit 4 • Better Together

© Macmillan/McGraw-Hill

Contents

Unit 5 • Growing and Changing

© Macmillan/McGraw-Hill

Contents

Unit 6 • The World Around Us

© Macmillan/McGraw-Hill

Name _____

The *a* in *cat* stands for the sound of short *a*.

The *i* in *pig* stands for the sound of short *i*.

Write the word from the box that names each picture.

| fan | crib | hat | crab | mitt | hand | pin | fish |

1. _____

2. _____

3. _____

4. _____

5. _____

6. _____

7. _____

8. _____

© Macmillan/McGraw-Hill

Name _____

A. Choose a word from the box to finish each sentence. Write the word on the line.

carefully	different	excited	groan	whisper

1. Tigers are _____ from lions because they have stripes.

2. Karen had to _____ when she talked in the library.

3. Emily was _____ to start school.

4. Juan _____ cut out the small pieces of paper.

5. I heard Taylor _____ when he finished the race.

B. Choose two words from the box. Then use each word in a sentence to tell about your first day of school. Write the sentences on the lines below.

6. _____

7. _____

© Macmillan/McGraw-Hill

Name _____

- A **question** is a sentence that asks something. It ends with a question mark.

- A **statement** is a sentence that tells something. It ends with a period.

- Begin each statement and question with a capital letter.

    Do you have a pencil?   I have paper.

Read the sentences. Circle each question, and underline each statement.

1. Do you have homework?

2. I have lots of homework.

3. What do you have to do?

4. I have to read a story.

5. The story is about a pig.

6. Does Frank have homework?

7. Frank has to write a story.

8. What kind of story will he write?

9. Will he write a funny story?

10. No, he will write a scary one.

© Macmillan/McGraw-Hill

Sometimes two **consonants** form a blend. In a consonant blend, you can hear the sound of each consonant.

Listen for the **blends** at the beginning of these words.

spoon   **sk**y

Listen for the **blends** at the end of these words.

toa**st**   ma**sk**

A. Circle the two pictures in each row whose names have the same beginning blend.

1.

2.

B. Circle the two pictures in each row whose names have the same blend at the end.

3.

4.

© Macmillan/McGraw-Hill

CA **R 1.0** Word Analysis, Fluency, and Systematic Vocabulary Development

| has | six | him | sat | bad |
| wag | if | will | had | fix |

A. Word Sort

Look at the spelling words in the box. Write the spelling words that have the short *a* sound.

1. _____ 2. _____ 3. _____

4. _____ 5. _____

Write the spelling words that have the short *i* sound.

6. _____ 7. _____ 8. _____

9. _____ 10. _____

B. Misfit Letter

An extra letter has been added to each spelling word below. Draw a line through the letter that does not belong. Write the word correctly on the line.

11. hais _____ 12. fixe _____

13. sayt _____ 14. hyim _____

15. whill _____ 16. iff _____

17. wage _____ 18. baid _____

19. sixe _____ 20. hayd _____

© Macmillan/McGraw-Hill

LC 1.8 Spell basic short-vowel, long-vowel, *r*- controlled, and consonant-blend patterns correctly.

Davids New Friends • **Grade 2/Unit 1** **13**

As you read *David's New Friends*, **fill in the
Character and Setting Chart.**

Character	Setting

How does the information you wrote in this Character
and Setting Chart help you analyze story structure in
David's New Friends?

© Macmillan/McGraw-Hill

 R 2.0 Reading Comprehension

> The **characters** are the people or animals in a story.
>
> The **setting** is where and when a story happens.

Read the passage below. Then write the answer to each question on the line.

It was the first day of school. Tim was worried. He saw the large playground and lots of children. He wondered if he would make new friends. When Tim heard the bell ring, he walked to his classroom. He sat at a desk next to a boy named Rob. Rob asked Tim if he would like to be friends. Tim was excited to have a new friend.

I. Who are the characters in the passage? _____

2. What is each character like?

_____

3. What is the setting of this passage? _____

_____

4. Write two sentences about your first day of school.

_____

_____

© Macmillan/McGraw-Hill

Dictionary entries are listed in **alphabetical order**. To help you put words in alphabetical order, think about where you would find them in the dictionary.

Write the following groups of words in alphabetical order.

1. friend _____

   trust _____

   nice _____

2. share _____

   caring _____

   sweet _____

3. dog _____

   game _____

   bed _____

4. love _____

   ice _____

   jump _____

5. teacher _____

   school _____

   principal _____

6. recess _____

   reading _____

   math _____

© Macmillan/McGraw-Hill

CA R 1.0 Word Analysis, Fluency, and Systematic Vocabulary Development

As I read, I will pay attention to the dialogue and how it affects my expression.

	"It's nearly time for our school fair," said Mr. Jeffs.
10	"What is our class doing?" asked Lucy.
17	"We could grow vegetables in our garden," said Sam.
26	"Then we could sell them," said Chico.
33	"It's too late," said Mr. Jeffs. "Potatoes, beans, and
42	carrots need time to grow."
47	Jing took a deep breath. "We could grow sprouts,"
56	she whispered.
58	"Sprouts?" said Mr. Jeffs. "That sounds interesting, Jing."
66	"We grow sprouts at home," said Jing. "They're ready
75	to eat in a few days."
81	"Sprouts!" Everyone was excited. "We'll grow sprouts!" 88

Comprehension Check

1. How can you tell that Jing is shy? **Character and Setting**

2. Why is Jing's solution a good idea? **Draw Conclusions**

	Words Read	−	Number of Errors	=	Words Correct Score
First Read		−		=	
Second Read		−		=	

© Macmillan/McGraw-Hill

CA **R 1.6** Read aloud fluently and accurately and with appropriate intonation and expression.

Captions are the words below a picture. They tell what the picture is about or explain what the people in it are saying or doing.

1. **Write a caption to go with this picture.**

_____

2. **Read the caption and draw a picture to go with it.**

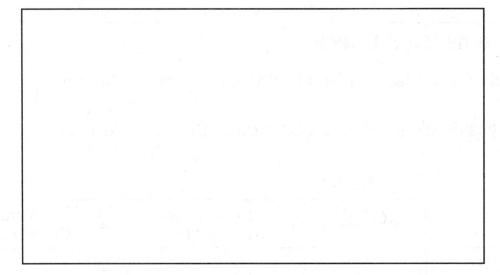

Recess is my favorite time of day.

 R 2.7 Interpret information from diagrams, charts, and graphs.

© Macmillan/McGraw-Hill

Name _____

- A sentence tells a complete thought.

- Begin each sentence with a capital letter.

- End a statement with a period.

- End a question with a question mark.

Read the passage. Circle each mistake in capitalization and punctuation. Then rewrite the passage correctly on the lines below.

Today is Monday What do we do first. the teacher Reads a story. then we have math. does each child have a pencil. Now we are ready to begin the lesson

_____

_____

_____

_____

© Macmillan/McGraw-Hill

A. There are six spelling mistakes in the paragraph below. Circle the misspelled words. Write the words correctly on the lines below.

I haid a very good day at school. I got to help fikx the fish tank. Then Mr. Dan and I sayt down. I told hime all about a book I had read. He asked iff he could borrow it. I said, "Yes, I wil bring it in so the whole class can read it."

I. _____ 2. _____ 3. _____

4. _____ 5. _____ 6. _____

Writing

B. Write about your day at school. Use three spelling words in your list.

_____

_____

_____

_____

© Macmillan/McGraw-Hill

CA **LC 1.8** Spell basic short-vowel, long-vowel, *r-* controlled, and consonant-blend patterns correctly.

Name _____

The letters *o*, *e*, and *u* can stand for a short vowel sound in the middle of a word.

Say the name of each picture. Write the name of the picture under the correct vowel sound.

top

cup

bed

sun

box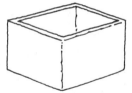

net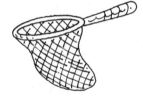

short *o*	short *e*	short *u*
1. _____	3. _____	5. _____
2. _____	4. _____	6. _____

© Macmillan/McGraw-Hill

Read the story. Choose words from the box to complete the sentences. Write the words on the lines. Then reread the story to check your answers.

| enjoyed | company | delighted | wonderful | share | thinning |

Maria's family liked to have visitors. _____ came

over often. Maria was always _____ to have her

friends and family at the house. She really _____

visits from her best friend, Lea. The two liked to _____
their books and play with Maria's dog. Maria always laughed
about the dog's hair on the floor. She said she could make a rug

from the _____ hair that had fallen out of its coat.

"That would make a _____ story," Lea said. "It could
be the best story ever. Let's start writing now!"

CA   R 1.0 Word Analysis, Fluency, and Systematic Vocabulary Development

© Macmillan/McGraw-Hill

Name _____

- An **exclamation** is a sentence that shows strong feelings. It ends with an exclamation point.

- Begin each exclamation with a capital letter.

  We love the zoo!
  Wow, those are huge elephants!

A. Underline each exclamation.

1. Today is Saturday.

2. Hooray, we are going to the zoo!

3. We will see many animals.

4. That giraffe is gigantic!

5. The lions look hungry.

6. Oh no, I'm scared!

7. The seals are so cute!

8. What time do you feed the seals?

9. The zoo closes in one hour.

10. We had so much fun!

B. Write two new exclamations on the lines.

_____

_____

© Macmillan/McGraw-Hill

Name _____

A **consonant digraph** is two consonants that together stand for only one sound. Say these words. Then listen for the sounds made by the letters in dark print.

thin   **sh**ed   **wh**en   **ch**op

Choose the group of letters from the box that completes each word. Write the letters on the line.

th   sh   wh   ch

1. I took a walk _____rough the park.

2. There was a _____ill in the wintry air.

3. I _____all find a fossil, I thought.

4. I looked for a long time but did not see a _____ing.

5. Then I saw a flat _____ite piece of rock with a pattern on it.

6. The pattern on the rock was in the _____ape of a leaf.

7. _____en I saw the leaf, I knew I was lucky.

8. My rock _____ip was a fossil!

© Macmillan/McGraw-Hill

CA R 1.0 Word Analysis, Fluency, and Systematic Vocabulary Development

Name _____

| went | tub | not | tug | fog |
| pet | tell | hut | job | bun |

Word Sort

A. Look at the spelling words in the box. Match each word to a vowel sound. Write the words on the lines.

Short *e*	Short *o*	Short *u*
I. _____	4. _____	7. _____
2. _____	5. _____	8. _____
3. _____	6. _____	9. _____
		10. _____

New Words

B. Make a new word from the spelling list by changing the vowel. Write the new word on the line.

II. $pat - a + e = $ _____   14. $fig - i + o = $ _____

12. $bin - i + u = $ _____   15. $hat - a + u = $ _____

13. $jab - a + o = $ _____

LC 1.8 Spell basic short-vowel, long-vowel, *r*-controlled, and consonant-blend patterns correctly.

Mr. Putter & Tabby Pour the Tea
Grade 2/Unit I   **25**

© Macmillan/McGraw-Hill

Name _____

**As you read *Mr. Putter & Tabby Pour the Tea*,
fill in the Story Map.**

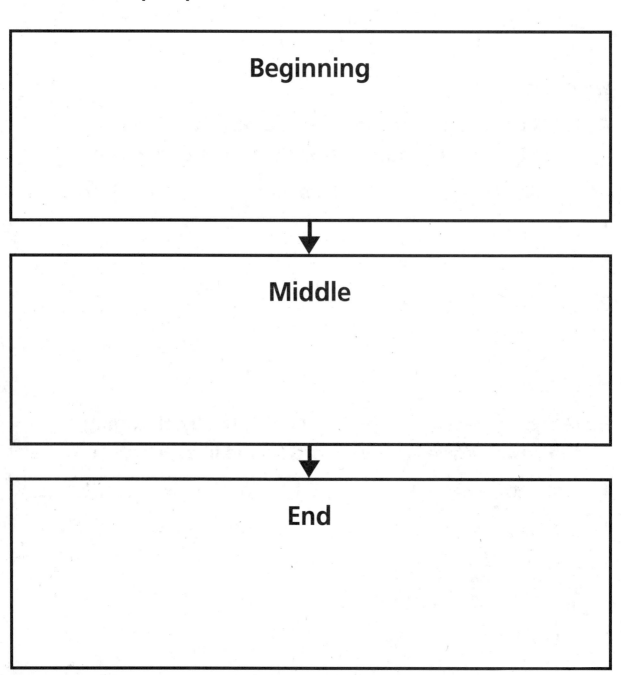

Beginning

Middle

End

How does the information you wrote in this Story Map
help you analyze story structure in *Mr. Putter & Tabby
Pour the Tea*?

© Macmillan/McGraw-Hill

CA **R 2.0** Reading Comprehension

Name _____

A **plot** contains a problem and a solution. Thinking about the plot can help you understand the story.

Read the passage. Answer the questions about the plot.

It was time to head home from school. Lee could not find his hat. He had seen Jim near the hats and coats earlier. "You took my hat," Lee said. Jim said he did not, but he would be happy to help Lee look for it.

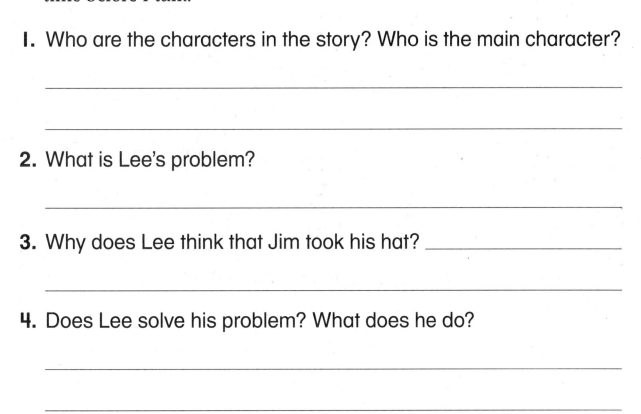

An angry Lee grabbed his coat to put it on. His hat fell out of his own coat pocket. "I'm sorry," he said to Jim. "I should have known you wouldn't take my hat. I'll think and look next time before I talk."

1. Who are the characters in the story? Who is the main character?

   _____

   _____

2. What is Lee's problem?

   _____

3. Why does Lee think that Jim took his hat? _____

   _____

4. Does Lee solve his problem? What does he do?

   _____

   _____

© Macmillan/McGraw-Hill

Verbs can have different **word endings**. These groups of letters can tell when something happens.

Underline the word that completes each sentence. Write the word on the line. Then circle the sentences that tell about the past.

1. Josie is always _____ to new people.
   talked   talking

2. After school, Jen _____ home with her new friends.
   walking   walked

3. Tim and Sam are still _____ outside.
   playing   played

4. Tammy _____ her mom if she could come over to my house.
   asking   asked

5. Grandma _____ the flowers I gave her.
   saved   saving

6. Lisa is _____ for Jim on the soccer field.
   waited   waiting

© Macmillan/McGraw-Hill

CA **R 1.0** Word Analysis, Fluency, and Systematic Vocabulary Development

Name _____

As I read, I will pay attention to the dialogue and how it affects my intonation.

	"Where does this path go?" asked Jasmine.
7	Just then, a butterfly flew past. It went down
16	the path.
18	"We should follow it!" said Jasmine.
24	"Okay," said Dad.
27	Jasmine pulled Dad up.
31	The butterfly led Jasmine and her dad into
39	a field.
41	"Wow!" she said. They saw a big bush. It was
51	covered in purple flowers and butterflies.
57	A woman was kneeling next to the bush.
65	"Excuse me," said Jasmine. "Why do butterflies
72	love this bush?"
75	"It is a butterfly bush," said the woman. 83

Comprehension Check

1. Why does Jasmine follow the butterfly? **Plot**

2. What do you think the woman is doing? **Make Inferences**

	Words Read	–	Number of Errors	=	Words Correct Score
First Read		–		=	
Second Read		–		=	

© Macmillan/McGraw-Hill

CA **R 1.6** Read aloud fluently and accurately and with appropriate intonation and expression.

Words that **rhyme** begin with different sounds and end with the same sounds.

    c**at**   p**at**   bl**ue**   tr**ue**

Rhythmic patterns are sounds and words that repeat to make a rhythm.

    Here we go round the mulberry bush, the mulberry bush, the mulberry bush.

Read the words to this old folk song. Then answer the questions below.

Hot cross buns, hot cross buns,

One a penny, two a penny, hot cross buns.

If you have no daughters, give them to your sons.

One a penny, two a penny, hot cross buns.

I. What words in this song rhyme?

_____

2. What two groups of words repeat to make a rhythmic pattern?

   a. _____

   b. _____

© Macmillan/McGraw-Hill

CA R 2.0 Reading Comprehension

Name _____

- Begin each sentence with a capital letter.
- End a **command** with a period and an **exclamation** with an exclamation point.

Circle each capitalization and punctuation mistake. Then rewrite the passage correctly on the lines.

let's go to our baseball game. you are up to bat first Watch out, here comes the ball. hit it hard. hooray, it's a home run.

_____

_____

_____

_____

© Macmillan/McGraw-Hill

A. There are six spelling mistakes in the letter below. Circle the misspelled words. Write the words correctly on the lines.

Dear Ben,

I want to tel you about Sam. He is my new peet rabbit. I weint to the store and got him a cage and some food. He is nat very big yet. I gave him his first bath in the tuab. Taking care of him is a big jaub. Please come see him soon!

Your friend,

Matt

1. _____ 2. _____ 3. _____

4. _____ 5. _____ 6. _____

B. Writing

Write a letter to a friend. Use three spelling words.

_____

_____

_____

_____

CA **LC 1.8** Spell basic short-vowel, long-vowel, *r*-controlled, and consonant-blend patterns correctly.

© Macmillan/McGraw-Hill

Practice

Phonics:
Final *e* (*a_e*), Contrast
with Short *a*

Name _____

> Short *a* is the vowel sound in the word *pat*.
>
> Long *a* is the vowel sound in the word *cake*.

Read the sentences below. Circle the word that completes each sentence. Then write the word on the line.

I. My mom baked us a _____.

cake
late
date

2. I was _____ when my best toy broke.

sad
pat
cap

3. My friends _____ me happy.

take
race
make

4. Please open the _____.

name
gate
fake

5. We put our books in this _____.

bag
sat
had

© Macmillan/McGraw-Hill

R 1.1 Recognize and use knowledge of spelling patterns
(e.g., diphthongs, special vowel spellings) when reading.

Their Native Tongue • Grade 2/Unit I   **33**

Name _____

A. Read the vocabulary words. Write the word that completes each sentence below.

| ancestors | heritage | local | native | reclaim | traditions |

1. My great-grandmother is one of my _____.

2. Picnics and parades on the Fourth of July are two American _____.

3. Ben was born in New York and is a _____ New Yorker.

4. The man gave away his tools but now he would like to _____ them.

5. Freedom is part of the American _____.

6. I did not want to go far, so I went to the _____ store for milk.

B. Write a sentence using one of the vocabulary words.

7. _____

_____

_____

_____

© Macmillan/McGraw-Hill

CA **R 1.0** Word Analysis, Fluency, and Systematic Vocabulary Development

- You can correct some incomplete sentences by adding a subject.
- A **subject** tells who or what does something.

Incomplete sentence: live at the firehouse

Complete sentence with a subject: The firefighters live at the firehouse.

Add a subject to the incomplete sentences and rewrite them on the lines below.

1. Visited the firehouse.

_____

2. Climbed inside a red fire truck.

_____

3. Taught us about fire safety.

_____

4. Told us to never play with matches.

_____

5. Told us to write about fire safety for homework.

_____

_____

© Macmillan/McGraw-Hill

CA **LC 1.1** Distinguish between complete and incomplete sentences.
LC 1.2 Recognize and use the correct word order in written sentences.

Name _____

A **consonant blend** is made when two consonants are blended together so that each sound is heard.

A. Choose words from the word box that have the same beginning blends as each of the words below. Write the words on the line.

skunk	drop	spill	slide
dream	skip	slim	spoon

1. drain _____ _____

2. spark _____ _____

3. skin _____ _____

4. slow _____ _____

B. Write the blend *sl*, *dr*, *sk*, or *sp* to complete each word.

5. Today the ____y is blue.

6. Why don't we ____ive to the beach?

7. We can find a sunny ____ot.

8. We may ____eep in the sun.

© Macmillan/McGraw-Hill

CA **R 1.1** Recognize and use knowledge of spelling patterns (e.g., diphthongs, special vowel spellings) when reading.

Practice

Spelling:
Final *e* (*a_e*), Contrast
with Short *a*

Name _____

| cape | bake | mad | bag | rake |
| ate | back | cap | ham | made |

A. Word Sort

Look at the spelling words in the box. Write the spelling
words that have the short *a* sound.

1. _____ 2. _____ 3. _____

4. _____ 5. _____

Write the spelling words that have the long *a* sound.

6. _____ 7. _____ 8. _____

9. _____ 10. _____

B. Word Find

Find and circle five spelling words in the puzzle.

```
a   b   q   p   t   k   e
a   m   a   c   x   u   d
t   a   i   g   f   y   l
e   d   c   q   r   s   h
y   e   g   b   a   c   k
u   q   x   v   k   x   j
z   t   l   w   e   m   n
```

© Macmillan/McGraw-Hill

LC 1.8 Spell basic short-vowel, long-vowel, *r*-controlled, and
consonant-blend patterns correctly.

Name _____

As you read _Their Native Tongue_, fill in the Main Idea and Details Web.

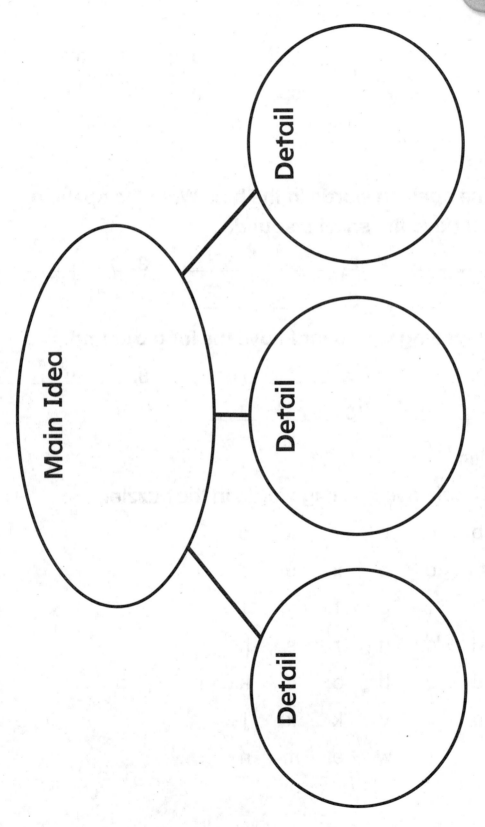

Main Idea

Detail

Detail

Detail

How does the information you wrote in this Main Idea and Details Web help you summarize _Their Native Tongue?_

_____

© Macmillan/McGraw-Hill

CA R 2.0 Reading Comprehension

The **main idea** is the most important message in a text. It is what the text is mostly about. **Details** are facts and bits of information. They tell more about the main idea.

Read the passage. Then circle the answer to each question.

Pete's family kept a special book. The book had hundreds of pages. It had information about the family's ancestors. Pete learned a lot about his family from the book. He found out that some ancestors had come over on the Mayflower. Later, other ancestors had traveled to Kansas. They had set up farms there. Still other family members had settled in California.

1. What is the main idea of this paragraph?

   a. Some of Pete's ancestors came over on the Mayflower.

   b. Pete learned about his family from the family book.

   c. Pete's family kept a special book.

2. Choose two details that tell about the main idea.

   a. Pete learned that some of his ancestors settled in California.

   b. Pete asked his parents about his ancestors.

   c. The book told about ancestors on the Mayflower.

© Macmillan/McGraw-Hill

Name _____

A **prefix** is a word part added to the beginning of a word to make a new word.

The prefix *un-* means "not."

The prefix *re-* means "again."

The prefix *dis-* means "opposite of."

Underline the words that have prefixes. Then write each word and its meaning.

1. Our family had an unlucky time last night.

_____

2. The fire in the fireplace went out, and we could not relight it.

_____

3. Somehow the dog managed to disconnect the TV.

_____

4. Somehow the garage door got locked. We could not get it unlocked.

_____

5. We were so busy that our food got cold. We had to reheat it.

_____

6. Why did so many things go wrong? We all disagree about the answer.

_____

© Macmillan/McGraw-Hill

CA　**R 1.9** Know the meaning of simple prefixes and suffixes (e.g., *over-, un-, -ing, -ly*).

As I read, I will pay attention to phrasing.

	Harry woke up. He rolled over and groaned.
8	Getting up early was the worst part of training for
18	team tryouts. Starting last week, he'd been jogging
26	every morning. He wanted to be a strong runner,
35	just like his mom.
39	After school, Harry met his dad at the basketball
48	courts. Harry's dad was a great basketball player.
56	Harry was training for the basketball team as well
65	as the track team!
69	The night before the tryouts, Harry went to bed
78	early. He stared at his uniform. He wondered if he
88	could ever be a track star. What if he could become
99	a basketball superstar, too? 103

Comprehension Check

1. What is Harry training for? **Main Idea and Details**

2. Why does Harry wonder if he could be a track or basketball star? **Make Inferences**

	Words Read	−	Number of Errors	=	Words Correct Score
First Read		−		=	
Second Read		−		=	

© Macmillan/McGraw-Hill

R 1.6 Read aloud fluently and accurately and with appropriate intonation and expression.

Name _____

The **title page** lists the name of the book, the author, and the publisher.

The **table of contents** lists the chapters in the book. It also tells the page numbers on which the chapters begin.

Read the title page and table of contents. Then complete each sentence below.

Life with Grandma Josie

by James Boto

Bookhouse Books

Table of Contents

1. The title of the book is _____.

2. The book was written by _____.

3. The book has _____ chapters.

4. Chapter 2 is titled _____.

5. Chapter 2 starts on page _____.

6. Chapter 3 is titled _____.

© Macmillan/McGraw-Hill

 R 2.0 Reading Comprehension

Name _____

Description Writing Frame

Summarize *Their Native Tongue*.
Use the Description Writing Frame below.

The Akwesasne Freedom School is an interesting school.

One interesting fact about the school is _____

_____

_____

_____

_____.

Another interesting fact about the school is _____

_____

_____

_____

_____.

Rewrite the completed summary on another sheet of paper. Keep it as a model for writing a summary of an article or selection using this text structure.

© Macmillan/McGraw-Hill

- Begin the greeting and closing of a letter with a capital letter.

- Use commas after the greeting and closing in a letter.

Rewrite the letter correctly on the lines below.

dear Mom and Dad

    am having a great time at camp. sing around the campfire. takes good care of us. can't wait for visiting day!
            love

            Maria

_____

_____

_____

_____

© Macmillan/McGraw-Hill

CA **LC 1.1** Distinguish between complete and incomplete sentences.
LC 1.2 Recognize and use the correct word order in written sentences.

Name _____
Practice

Spelling:
Final *e* (*a_e*), Contrast
with Short *a*

**A. There is one spelling mistake in each sentence.
Circle the misspelled words. Write the correct words
on the lines below.**

1. Dad and I got a baig.

2. We went backe to camp with lots of sticks.

3. Dad made a fire, and we ayt fish for dinner.

4. I was maed when it started to rain.

5. We mayd sure the fire was out.

1. _____   2. _____   3. _____

4. _____   5. _____

B. Writing

**Write about fire safety. Use three
spelling words from your list.**

_____

_____

_____

_____

© Macmillan/McGraw-Hill

LC 1.8 Spell basic short-vowel, long-vowel, *r*-controlled, and
consonant-blend patterns correctly.

Their Native Tongue • **Grade 2/Unit I** **45**

Short *i* is the vowel sound in the word *pig*.

Long *i* is the vowel sound in the word *bike*.

Circle the word that completes the sentence. Then write it on the line.

I. The sun will _____ in the east.

                                  rinse
                                  rise

2. My birthday is _____ days from today.

                                  nine
                                  nice

3. I _____ a home run!

                                  hit
                                  hike

4. Let's _____ from the raft to the beach.

                                  smile
                                  swim

5. They like to play _____ and seek.

                                  hid
                                  hide

6. Put the dog's water _____ next to his food bowl.   dine
                                                                    dish

© Macmillan/McGraw-Hill

CA R 1.0 Word Analysis, Fluency, and Systematic Vocabulary Development

Name _____

Choose a word from the box to complete each sentence. Then write the word on the line.

signing	cultures	relatives
celebrate	deaf	

I. My _____ came over for a family dinner.

_____

2. Lily wants to _____ her birthday at the park.

_____

3. Lana can't hear. She goes to a school for _____ children.

_____

4. Aunt Tina travels all around the world to meet people from

different _____. _____

5. Randy's parents are talking with their hands. They are _____.

_____

© Macmillan/McGraw-Hill

- A **predicate** tells what the subject of a sentence does or is.

- You can correct some incomplete sentences by adding a predicate.

  Incomplete sentence: My dad

  Complete sentence: My dad loves vanilla ice cream.

Draw lines to match each subject with a predicate to make a complete sentence. Then write the sentences on the lines below.

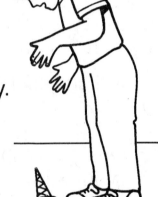

1. An ice-cream truck   dropped his cone.

2. The driver   ate her cone quickly.

3. Mia   drove into the park.

4. Sam   sold ice cream.

1. _____

2. _____

3. _____

4. _____

CA **LC 1.0** Written and Oral English Language Conventions

© Macmillan/McGraw-Hill

Name _____

The **c** in **cent** stands for the /**s**/ sound. This is **soft c**.

The **g** in **gem** stands for the /**j**/ sound. This is **soft g**.

garden	camp	circle	giant	face	h u g e
city	cent	go	car	gentle	germs

Circle the words in the box that have the soft *c* or soft *g* sound. Then choose one of the circled words to complete each sentence. Write it on the line.

1. My friend Jim and I live in a big _____.

2. It is hard to buy anything for just one _____.

3. The puppy grew into a _____ dog.

4. My friend drew a round _____ on the paper.

5. Dad seemed as big as a _____ to my little brother.

6. Wash your hands often to get rid of _____.

7. My friend had a big smile on his happy _____.

8. Ann gave my head a _____ pat.

© Macmillan/McGraw-Hill

CA **R 1.1** Recognize and use knowledge of spelling patterns
(e.g., diphthongs, special vowel spellings) when reading.

Name _____

hike	did	rip	pipe	side
fin	mix	line	five	pick

Word Sort

A. Look at the spelling words in the box. Write the spelling words that have the short *i* sound.

1. _____   2. _____   3. _____

4. _____   5. _____

B. Write the spelling words that have the long *i* sound.

6. _____   7. _____   8. _____

9. _____   10. _____

Sounds the Same

C. Write the spelling word that rhymes with each word below.

11. bike _____   16. dive _____

12. bin _____   17. stick _____

13. kid _____   18. ride _____

14. ripe _____   19. fix _____

15. fine _____   20. dip _____

CA LC 1.8 Spell basic short-vowel, long-vowel, *r*-controlled, and consonant-blend patterns correctly.

© Macmillan/McGraw-Hill

Name _____

As you read *Meet Rosina*, fill in the Main Idea and
Details Web.

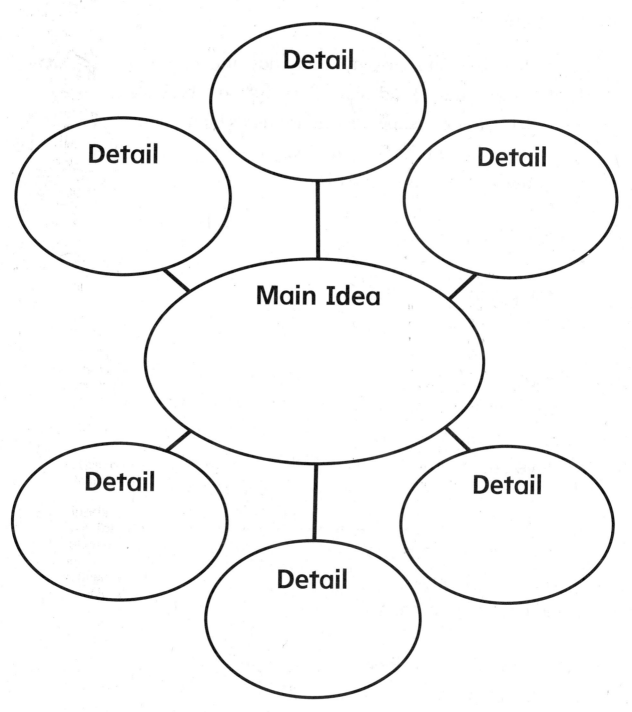

How does the information you wrote in this Main Idea and
Details Web help you summarize *Meet Rosina*?

© Macmillan/McGraw-Hill

 R 2.0 Reading Comprehension

Read the passage. Then circle the word or group of words that completes each sentence. Write the answers on the lines.

Jack likes baseball. He plays every day after school. He also plays on weekends. Jack likes first base best. He plays first base for the town team. He reads books about baseball. In the summer he plays ball at sports camp. Jack wants to be a baseball player when he grows up.

1. The story is all about _____.
   a. Jack
   b. how to play baseball
   c. sports camp

2. After school, Jack _____.
   a. watches TV
   b. goes to camp
   c. plays baseball

3. Jack likes _____ best.
   a. reading about baseball
   b. playing first base
   c. playing second base

4. When he grows up, Jack wants to be a _____.
   a. baseball player
   b. baseball coach
   c. sports writer

© Macmillan/McGraw-Hill

 R 2.0 Reading Comprehension

A **dictionary** lists words and their meanings. Some words have more than one meaning.

Use the dictionary definition to find the correct definition for the word *sign* in each sentence. Write the number of the definition on the line. Then write whether *sign* is used as a *noun* or *verb*.

 sign (sine) *noun* **1.** A symbol that means or stands for something: *This sign means add: +.* **2.** Something written, such as a poster, that gives information: *This sign means the street goes one way.*
verb **3.** To write your name: *Please sign on the dotted line.*
4. To use American Sign Language: *I can sign the word* dog.

I. That movie star will <u>sign</u> pictures for her fans.

   In this sentence, *sign* means _____

2. The <u>sign</u> says we should turn left.

   In this sentence, *sign* means _____

3. They <u>sign</u> to each other across the room.

   In this sentence, *sign* means _____

4. This is the <u>sign</u> for cents: ¢.

   In this sentence, *sign* means _____

© Macmillan/McGraw-Hill

R 1.0 Word Analysis, Fluency, and Systematic Vocabulary Development

As I read, I will pay attention to phrasing.

	People who are deaf cannot hear. They need to
9	talk and listen without using sounds.
15	Deaf people communicate in many ways.
21	A language that is often used by deaf people is
31	called sign language.
34	Sign language uses signs for words. Signs are
42	made using hand shapes and movements.
48	One way of signing is to spell out a word. There is
60	a sign for each letter of the alphabet.
68	Another way to sign is to show a whole word. 78

Comprehension Check

1. What is this passage about? **Main Idea and Details**

2. How do people use signs to communicate? **Main Idea
and Details**

	Words Read	–	Number of Errors	=	Words Correct Score
First Read		–		=	
Second Read		–		=	

© Macmillan/McGraw-Hill

R 1.6 Read aloud fluently and accurately and with appropriate intonation and expression.

Name _____

Words that **rhyme** begin with different sounds but end with the same sound.

Read the poem. Circle the words that rhyme. Then finish the poem.

We are different, you and I.

I like peanuts in my pie.

You like cake.

You love to bake.

We are special, you and I.

We are different, you and I.

_____

_____

_____

_____

© Macmillan/McGraw-Hill

- Use a comma between the day and year in a date.
- Use a comma between the names of a city and a state.

Draw a line below each mistake in the letter.
Then rewrite the letter correctly on the lines.

Dear Uncle Ted,

    I can't wait to visit you in Los Angeles California! We are coming on December 23 2007. I'll be sad when we leave there on January 2 2008.

    It is so cold here in Burlington Vermont! The snow.

          Love,

          Noah

_____

_____

_____

_____

_____

_____

© Macmillan/McGraw-Hill

CA **LC 1.0** Written and Oral English Language Conventions

Name _____

A. There are six spelling mistakes in the list below. Circle the misspelled words. Write the words correctly on the lines.

Things I Can Do

1. I can hik up a big hill.

2. I can mixx red and yellow paint.

3. I can spell the word lien.

4. I can clean up my sied of the room.

5. I can pik up my little sister.

6. I can count down from fiv.

1. _____   2. _____   3. _____

4. _____   5. _____   6. _____

Writing

B. Make a list of things you can do all by yourself. Use four words from the spelling list.

_____

_____

_____

_____

LC 1.8 Spell basic short-vowel, long-vowel, *r-* controlled, and consonant-blend patterns correctly.

Meet Rosina • **Grade 2/Unit I**   **57**

Name _____

The **o_e** in **nose** stands for the long **o** sound.

The **u_e** in **cube** stands for the long **u** sound.

**Circle the word that completes each sentence.
Then write the word on the line.**

1. The bunny likes to _____.

   hut   hop   hope

2. This flower is a _____ .

   lot   rose   top

3. Planting seeds is a lot of _____.

   hug   fume   fun

4. Mary squeezed the _____ of toothpaste.

   tub   tube   huge

5. Brett is cleaning with a _____.

   map   mope   mop

6. Keith is learning to play the _____ .

   flute   fuse   fluff

7. The _____ has a bad odor when it lifts its tail.

   stink   skunk   stock

8. Tandy is writing a _____ to Sam.

   pot   not   note

© Macmillan/McGraw-Hill

 R 1.1 Recognize and use knowledge of spelling patterns
(e.g., diphthongs, special vowel spellings) when reading.

Name _____

Read the story. Choose words from the box to complete the sentences. Then write the answers on the lines.

| cuddle | favorite | patient | practiced | settled | wrinkled |

At my house, we have two fish and a dog.

They are all great pets, but Max the dog

is my _____. Max

_____ his nose when he

smelled dinner yesterday. He likes to _____ with

me when I read. After he gets _____ on my lap,

he falls asleep. I got Max when he was a puppy. I taught him how

to sit and stay. We _____ the tricks every day

until Max knew how to do them. It took a long time, so I had to

be _____. Now Max does them all the time, even

when I don't ask him to!

© Macmillan/McGraw-Hill

Name _____

- If two sentences have subjects that are the same, you can combine the sentences.
- You can combine sentences by joining the predicates with **and**.

    Aki was born in Japan.   Aki lives in America.

    Aki was born in Japan and lives in America.

Combine the predicates in each pair of sentences to make one sentence. Write the new sentence on the line.

1. Aki speaks Japanese.   Aki writes in English.

   _____

2. Aki has brown hair.   Aki is tall.

   _____

3. Emily sat next to Aki.   Emily shared her snack.

   _____

4. Aki plays basketball.   Aki jumps rope.

   _____

© Macmillan/McGraw-Hill

CA **LC 1.0** Written and Oral English Language Conventions

Name _____

Write a word from the box to answer each clue.

leash	booth	graph	stitches
pitcher	mashed	mouth	teacher

1. You may sit here in a diner

   or restaurant. _____

2. Some people like their potatoes

   made this way. _____

3. Use this when walking the dog. _____

4. You can learn a lot from this person. _____

5. Fix a rip in your clothes with these. _____

6. You look at this for information. _____

7. You use this when you talk and eat. _____

8. This baseball player throws the ball to the batter.

   _____

© Macmillan/McGraw-Hill

R 1.1 Recognize and use knowledge of spelling patterns
(e.g., diphthongs, special vowel spellings) when reading.

| hot | lock | fox | home | nose |
| box | poke | rope | pot | cone |

A. Word Sort

Look at the spelling words in the box. Write the spelling words that have the short *o* sound.

1. _____ 2. _____ 3. _____

4. _____ 5. _____

Write the spelling words that have the long *o* sound.

6. _____ 7. _____ 8. _____

9. _____ 10. _____

B. Misfit Letter

An extra letter has been added to each spelling word below. Draw a line through the letter that does not belong. Write the word correctly on the line.

11. foxe _____ 12. roope _____

13. doag _____ 14. coine _____

15. homme _____ 16. boxx _____

17. nosie _____ 18. locke _____

19. pout _____ 20. poeke _____

© Macmillan/McGraw-Hill

LC 1.8 Spell basic short-vowel, long-vowel, *r*-controlled, and consonant-blend patterns correctly.

As you read *My Name Is Yoon*, fill in the Predictions Chart.

What I Predict	What Happens

How does the information you wrote in this Predictions Chart
help you summarize *My Name Is Yoon*?

© Macmillan/McGraw-Hill

 R 2.0 Reading Comprehension

You can use what you know and what has happened in a story to **make predictions**. Predictions are good guesses about what might happen next in a story.

Read the paragraph. Then circle the sentence that tells what will probably happen next. Write a sentence to explain your prediction.

Umi looked at the new house. It was so different. There were heavy wooden doors. She missed the light paper doors of her old home. There were cold tile and wood floors. She missed the light bamboo floors of her old home. Umi's father answered a knock at the door. A family came in with a cake. The girl smiled shyly. "My name is Kate. Want to play?" Umi smiled back.

a. Umi will make a new friend.

b. Umi will cry.

c. Umi will move to a new house.

_____

What do you think will happen next?

_____

© Macmillan/McGraw-Hill

A **verb** is an action word. To show that action took place in the past, **-ed** is added to the verb.

Underline the verb in each sentence. Then change each verb so that it tells about the past. Write the new word on the line.

1. I wash the dog on Saturdays. _____

2. My parents clean the yard. _____

3. I love my science class. _____

4. The teachers plan our class parties. _____

5. We like the new teacher. _____

6. Puppies wag their tails. _____

7. The students talk about the class trip. _____

8. We hope for sunny skies. _____

Name _____

As I read, I will pay attention to my expression.

	"We have to leave Ireland," said Mam. "We have a
10	family to look after, and not enough food."
18	"We should go to North America like the Sullivans,"
27	said Dad.
29	I thought of how Fergus Sullivan always bragged about
38	going to America. Then we never heard from him after
48	he went across the Atlantic Ocean!
54	"Your Uncle Paddy will help us get settled there,"
63	said Dad.
65	Uncle Paddy is my favorite uncle. If he was brave
75	enough to go to America, I can be brave, too. 85

Comprehension Check

I. Why does the family have to leave Ireland? **Main Idea and Details**

2. What do you think will happen once the family moves to America? **Make and Confirm Predictions**

	Words Read	–	Number of Errors	=	Words Correct Score
First Read		–		=	
Second Read		–		=	

© Macmillan/McGraw-Hill

CA R 1.6 Read aloud fluently and accurately and with appropriate intonation and expression.

Name _____

> **Bar graphs** show the relationship between numbers using bars of different lengths.

Read the bar graph. Circle the correct answer to each question.

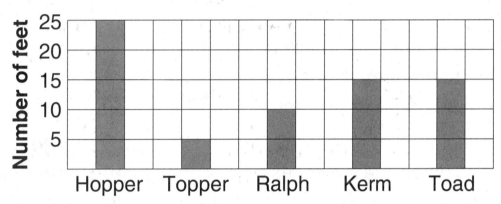

Distance Frogs Jumped

I. What is being compared?

   a. color of frogs   **b.** how far each frog jumped

2. Which frog jumped the farthest?

   a. Kerm   **b.** Hopper   **c.** Topper   **d.** Toad

3. Which frog jumped the least distance?

   a. Kerm   **b.** Hopper   **c.** Topper   **d.** Toad

4. Which two frogs jumped the same distance?

   a. Kerm and Hopper   **b.** Topper and Toad   **c.** Kerm and Toad

5. Which frog jumped 10 feet?

   a. Kerm   **b.** Ralph   **c.** Hopper   **d.** Topper

© Macmillan/McGraw-Hill

CA R 2.7 Interpret information from diagrams, charts, and graphs.

- Sometimes you can combine sentences by joining two subjects or two predicates with **and**.

- Use quotation marks at the beginning and end of what a person says.

Write the passage correctly on the lines. Add quotation marks where they are needed. Combine sentences that have the same subjects or predicates.

Miguel moved to Austin, Texas. His family moved to Austin, Texas. He starts his new school soon. He starts his new soccer team soon. Miguel is worried.

I miss my friends, Miguel said.

You will make new friends, said his mom.

_____

_____

_____

_____

_____

© Macmillan/McGraw-Hill

CA **LC 1.0** Written and Oral English Language Conventions

A. There are five spelling mistakes in the paragraph below. Circle the misspelled words. Write the words correctly on the lines below.

Dad and I planted seeds at hoem today. Dad put dirt in a big pott. The first thing I did was pokke little holes in the dirt. Then we put the seeds in the holes. We put the pot in the sun where my dogg could not get it. He likes to sniff every thing with his big noes!

I. _____   2. _____   3. _____

4. _____   5. _____

B. Writing

Write about planting or taking care of seeds. Use five spelling words from your list.

_____

_____

_____

_____

_____

© Macmillan/McGraw-Hill

LC 1.8 Spell basic short-vowel, long-vowel, *r*-controlled, and consonant-blend patterns correctly.

My Name Is Yoon • Grade 2/Unit I   69

Name _____

The letters **ai** and **ay** can stand for the long **a** sound.
Listen for the long **a** sound as you say the word **braid**.
Listen for the long **a** sound as you say the word **day**.

Read each sentence. Then write the letters *ai* or *ay* on the lines to complete each word.

I. Tod_____ I will go to the doctor.

2. Dad and I will take a tr_____n there.

3. Dad said I could p_____ the clerk for the train tickets.

4. He will w_____t with me in the doctor's office.

5. Mom m_____ come, too.

6. A sitter will st_____ with my little sister.

7. Mom has p_____d the sitter already.

8. We'll read our m_____l when we get home.

© Macmillan/McGraw-Hill

CA R 1.1 Recognize and use knowledge of spelling patterns
(e.g., diphthongs, special vowel spellings) when reading.

A. Choose the word from the box that best completes the sentence. Write it on the line.

| figure | vendors | concern | collection | exclaimed |

1. My _____ for the picnic is that it may rain.

2. "What a beautiful rainbow!" Kate _____.

3. The craft _____ set up their goods on tables on the sidewalk.

4. I can carve an animal _____ out of wood.

5. I have a _____ of dolls from all over the world.

B. Write two sentences using as many words from the box as you can.

6. _____

_____

7. _____

_____

Name _____

- A noun is a word that names a person, place, or thing.

- Some nouns name **places**.

  This is my <u>backyard</u>.

- Some nouns name **things**.

  The <u>flowers</u> are yellow.

A. Read the sentences. Underline the nouns that name things. Circle the nouns that name places.

1. Many plants grow in the forest.

2. We saw evergreens in the mountains.

3. You can see a cactus in the desert.

4. What trees grow in your town?

B. Write two more sentences on the lines below. In one sentence, include a noun that names a place. In the other sentence, include a noun that names a thing.

5. _____

_____

6. _____

_____

© Macmillan/McGraw-Hill

LC 1.3 Identify and correctly use various parts of speech, including nouns and verbs, in writing and speaking.

Name _____

Some words begin with three consonants. The words
street, scrub, and **spray** all begin with three consonant
sounds. Blend the consonant sounds together so that
each sound is heard.

s t r eet →   **s c r** ub →   **s p r** ay →

**Read the name of each picture. Find words from the box that
begin with the same sounds. Write the words on the lines.**

scream	sprain	scrape	stream	scrub	spray
string	splint	street	strict	screen	strap

sprinkler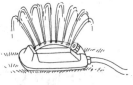

1. _____   2. _____

screw

3. _____   4. _____

straw

5. _____   6. _____

© Macmillan/McGraw-Hill

 R 1.1 Recognize and use knowledge of spelling patterns (e.g.,
diphthongs, special vowel spellings) when reading.

Name _____

jay	may	wait	sail	train
hay	main	tail	pay	stay

A. Write the Words

Write the spelling words that have the long *a* sound spelled *ai*.

1. _____ 2. _____ 3. _____

4. _____ 5. _____

Write the spelling words that have the long *a* sound spelled *ay*.

6. _____ 7. _____ 8. _____

9. _____ 10. _____

B. New Words

Make a new word from the spelling list by changing the first letter.

11. way − w + j = _____

12. mail − m + t = _____

13. day − d + h = _____

14. gain − g + m = _____

15. brain − b + t = _____

LC 1.8 Spell basic short-vowel, long-vowel, *r*- controlled, and consonant-blend patterns correctly.

© Macmillan/McGraw-Hill

As you read *Babu's Song,* fill in the Character, Setting, and Plot Chart.

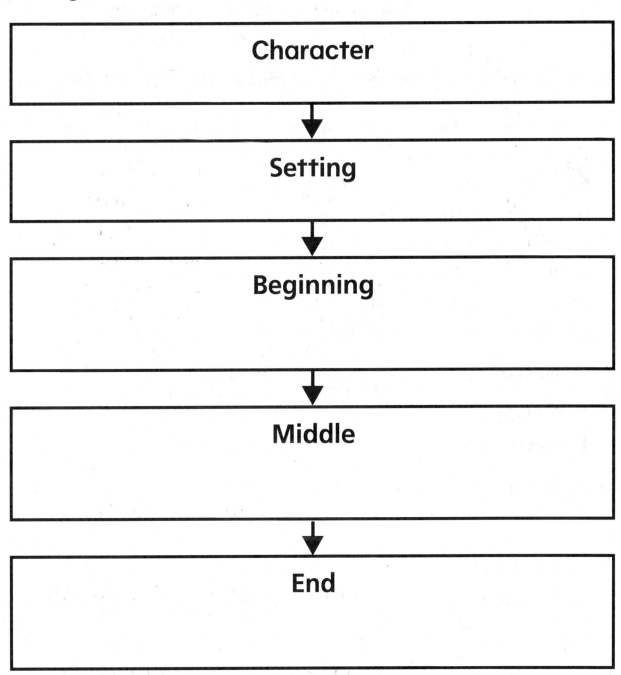

Character

Setting

Beginning

Middle

End

How does the information you wrote in this Character, Setting, and Plot Chart help you to better understand *Babu's Song*?

© Macmillan/McGraw-Hill

Analyzing the **setting** helps you understand how the place and time affect what the characters do and say.

Read the story. Then circle the best answer to each question.

It was so hot! Even though it was early morning, Trista's clothes were already too heavy for the heat. Trista pushed through the door of the small clothing shop. The woman behind the counter smiled at her and asked her something in a language Trista could not understand. Trista pointed to one of the cool cotton outfits and pointed to herself hopefully. The woman smiled, looked through a rack of clothing, and pulled out an outfit that was just her size. Ten minutes later Trista was back in the street, cooler, and happier.

I. Trista is a: ____

   a. woman

   b. wild animal

   c. young boy

2. Trista probably: ____

   a. visits this place all the time

   b. does not like this place

   c. has not visited this place often

3. She seems to be in: ____

   a. her hometown

   b. a foreign country

   c. a zoo

4. This story takes place: ____

   a. in a place that is very hot

   b. in a place that is cold

   c. in a forest

© Macmillan/McGraw-Hill

CA **R 2.0** Reading Comprehension

Name _____

> To figure out the meaning of a word, look at how it is used in the sentence. Use **context clues** in the surrounding sentences to help you figure out the meaning.

Use words from the box to make the story make sense. You will not use all the words.

grandfather	grew	mother	Korea
friends	plane	boat	Texas

Today my _____ came to visit. He lives in

Korea. Korea is where my father _____ up. You

can still hear his old language in his accent when he speaks

his new language, English. My _____ grew up in

_____. You can hear that when she speaks, too.

My grandfather wants my mother and me to see

_____. My grandfather will stay here for two

weeks. He will see my school, meet my _____,

and watch me play soccer in the afternoons. Then my whole

family will get on a _____ and fly to Korea.

There, we will see where my father went to school and meet

some of his old friends.

© Macmillan/McGraw-Hill

As I read, I will pay attention to my expression.

	Soccer wasn't just a game to Carlos. It was his whole life.
12	His father worked among the **vendors** at the local soccer
22	ground. He owned a little stall that sold meat empanadas and
33	fresh fruit juices. Carlos went along with him every Saturday
43	to watch the village team play.
49	Carlos and his friends practiced before and after school
58	every day. On the weekends they played games against
67	neighboring villages.
69	Their team was called the Mighty Lions. But they hadn't
79	been too mighty lately. In fact, they had lost every game
90	so far this season.
94	Paulo was the best player on their team. He dreamed of
105	being a Brazilian soccer star, like Pelé and Ronaldo.
114	"I'm going to score 1,000 goals," he said. "And help Brazil
124	add another three World Cups to its **collection**!" 132

Comprehension Check

I. How have the Mighty Lions done so far this season? **Character and Setting**

2. Was Paulo a great soccer champion like Pelé and Ronaldo? **Character and Setting**

	Words Read	–	Number of Errors	=	Words Correct Score
First Read		–		=	
Second Read		–		=	

© Macmillan/McGraw-Hill

CA R 1.6 Read aloud fluently and accurately and with appropriate intonation and expression.

Name _____

A **map** is a drawing. It shows where places are.

Read the map. Then follow the directions and circle the best answer for each question.

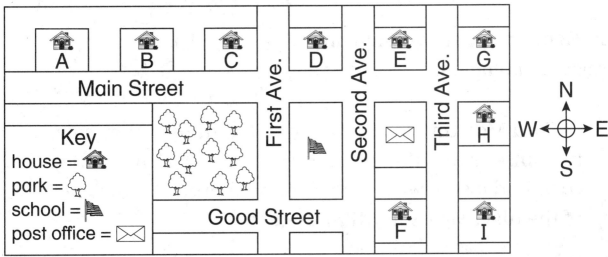

1. Color the key yellow.

2. Color the school blue.

3. Color the post office red.

4. What place is shown on this map?

   a. New York City   **b.** Quiet Town   **c.** a state park

5. What kind of building does ✉ represent?

   a. post office   **b.** school   **c.** store

6. If you lived in house A, how could you get to school?

_____

© Macmillan/McGraw-Hill

CA R 2.7 Interpret information from diagrams, charts, and graphs.

Babu's Song • Grade 2/Unit 2   **79**

Name _____

> - A noun is a word that names a person, place, or thing.
>
> - Use commas to separate three or more words in a series.

A. Read the passage. Add any missing commas.

Cara Max and Jack hiked up a mountain. They saw trees insects and flowers along the path. For lunch they each had a sandwich a yogurt and a drink. At the end of the hike, Max said, "I'm tired!"

B. Go back and underline each noun in the passage. Write all the nouns on the lines below.

_____   _____   _____

_____   _____   _____

_____   _____   _____

_____   _____   _____

_____   _____   _____

© Macmillan/McGraw-Hill

CA
LC 1.3 Identify and correctly use various parts of speech, including nouns and verbs, in writing and speaking.
LC 1.4 Use commas in the greeting and closure of a letter and with dates and items in a series.

Name _____

A. There are five spelling mistakes in the paragraph below. Circle the misspelled words. Write the words correctly on the lines below.

Today my mom fell and hurt her arm. My dad thought she mae need a cast. We all went to the hospital. We needed to see the mayn doctor. We had to waet our turn. Then my mom got an X ray. She did need a cast. The doctor told her to staiy still. My dad left to paye the bill. At last, we all went home and signed mom's new cast.

I. _____ 2. _____ 3. _____

4. _____ 5. _____

B. Writing

Write about how you would help someone who got hurt or who was sick. Use five spelling words from your list.

_____

_____

_____

_____

_____

LC 1.8 Spell basic short-vowel, long-vowel, *r*- controlled, and consonant-blend patterns correctly.

Babu's Song • **Grade 2/Unit 2**   **81**

© Macmillan/McGraw-Hill

Name _____

The letters **e**, **ee**, **ea**, **ey**, and **y** can stand for the long **e** sound.

w**e**   f**ee**t   m**ea**t   k**ey**   happ**y**

Write the missing letter or letters to complete each word.

1.

t_____

2.

m_____

3.

str_____t

4.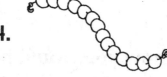

b_____ds

5.

bab_____

6.

mon_____

7.

donk_____

8.

lad_____

 CA   R 1.1 Recognize and use knowledge of spelling patterns (e.g., diphthongs, special vowel spellings) when reading.

© Macmillan/McGraw-Hill

Read the story. Choose words from the box to complete the sentences. Then write the answers on the lines.

| eager | glaring | lap | thorny | finally | peeked |

Mrs. Dru works at the animal shelter. She is _____

to find homes for the animals there.

One day I visited the shelter. Some kittens were playing in

the sun near some _____ rosebushes. The mama cat

watched her kittens play. When I reached down to pick up a

kitten, I saw the mama _____ at me. "Don't worry,"

I said to her. "I won't hurt your babies!" One little kitten

_____ up at me. It melted my heart. I watched the

kitten _____ up some water with its pink tongue.

I begged my parents to let me have the kitten. After a long

time, they _____ said I could take the kitten home.

© Macmillan/McGraw-Hill

Name _____

- Add **-es** to form the plural of singular nouns that end in **s**, **sh**, **ch**, or **x**.

    fox———→foxes   lunch ———→lunches

- To form the plural of nouns ending in a consonant and **y**, change **y** to **i** and add **-es**.

                    pony ———→ponies

- Some nouns change their spelling to name more than one.

    mouse———→mice   man———→men

Read the sentences. Make the underlined nouns plural. Write them on the lines.

1. The <u>child</u> took a trip to the farm. _____

2. How many <u>bus</u> did they fill up? _____

3. The <u>pony</u> were eating grass. _____

4. Several <u>mouse</u> were in the barn. _____

5. For five <u>penny</u> they could feed the animals. _____

© Macmillan/McGraw-Hill

CA LC 1.0 Written and Oral English Language Conventions

A **prefix** is a word part added to the beginning of a word to make a new word.

- The prefix **re-** means "again."
- The prefixes **dis-** and **un-** mean "not" or "the opposite of."

Combine a prefix from the box with each word below. Form a word that fits the sentence.

un-	re-	dis-

able   I. Some kids at school are _____ to speak English.

turns   2. Mr. Flora _____ day after day to help these kids after school.

teach   3. He finds out what kids don't understand. Then he tries to _____ things in a new way.

agrees   4. People say that Mr. Flora works too hard, but he _____.

read   5. Mr. Flora will read and _____ books with kids.

pleased   6. He is only _____ if kids don't try to learn.

© Macmillan/McGraw-Hill

R 1.9 Know the meaning of simple prefixes and suffixes (e.g., *over-, un-, -ing, -ly*).

Tomás and the Library Lady **85**
Grade 2/Unit 2

Name _____

| need | baby | we | queen | eat |
| leaf | he | mean | seek | pony |

A. Word Sort

Fill in the blanks below with spelling words that match each spelling pattern.

e	*ee*	*ea*	*y*
1. _____	3. _____	6. _____	9. _____
2. _____	4. _____	7. _____	10. _____
	5. _____	8. _____	

B. New Words

Make a new word from the spelling list by changing the first letter.

11. seed – s + n _____

12. be – b + w _____

13. lean – l + m _____

14. me – m + h _____

15. peek – p + s _____

CA **LC 1.8** Spell basic short-vowel, long-vowel, *r*-controlled, and consonant-blend patterns correctly.

© Macmillan/McGraw-Hill

Name _____

As you read *Tomás and the Library Lady*, fill in the Cause and Effect Chart.

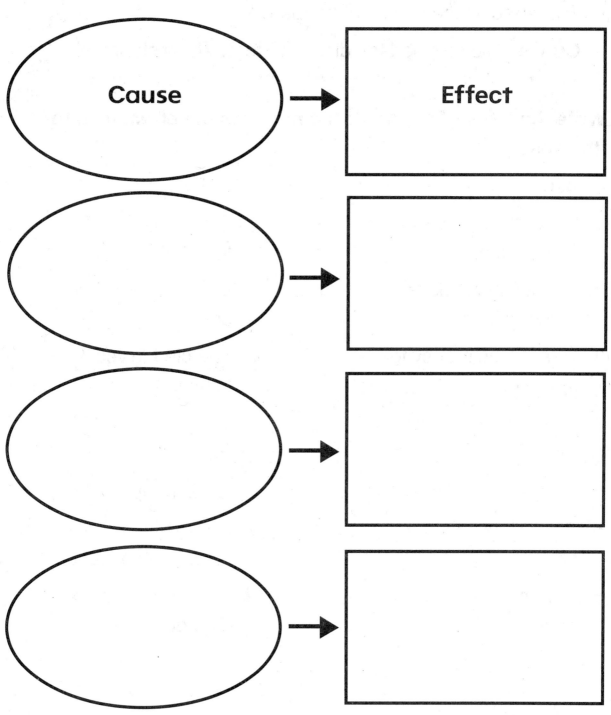

How does the information you wrote in this Cause and Effect Chart help you retell *Tomás and the Library Lady*?

© Macmillan/McGraw-Hill

CA **R 2.6** Recognize cause-and-effect relationships in a text.

Tomás and the Library Lady
Grade 2/Unit 2
87

Name _____

The **cause** is what makes something happen.
The **effect** is the thing that happens.

Cause: Ana dropped the dish.   **Effect:** The dish broke.

Write the letter of the sentence that tells the effect next to its cause.

Cause	Effect
1. Li wants to raise money for her club. _____	**a.** The club is thankful.
2. Li takes the cans to the grocery store. _____	**b.** Li collects tin cans.
3. Li gives the money to the club. _____	**c.** The clerk gives Li money.

Cause	Effect
4. Sal's mother is sick. _____	**d.** Sal is happy.
5. Sal makes some soup. _____	**e.** Sal wants to make his mom feel better.
6. Sal's mother feels better. _____	**f.** Sal's mother drinks the soup.

© Macmillan/McGraw-Hill

CA R 2.6 Recognize cause-and-effect relationships in a text.

Name _____

> **Multiple-meaning words** are words that have more than one meaning. You can look at the other words in the sentence to help you decide which meaning of the word fits best in the sentence.

Read each sentence. Then write the meaning of the underlined word.

1. I will take gymnastics in the <u>fall</u>.

_____

2. I was careful not to <u>fall</u> down.

_____

3. My mom looked at her <u>watch</u> to make sure we were not late.

_____

4. I like to <u>watch</u> my dog chase his tail.

_____

5. Your heart is in your <u>chest</u>.

_____

6. I keep my toys in a wood <u>chest</u>.

_____

© Macmillan/McGraw-Hill

As I read, I will pay attention to intonation.

	Kenny and Grandfather sat together on the porch.
8	They could hear the frogs singing in the pond behind the fence.
20	"Have the frogs sung every summer?" Kenny asked Grandfather.
29	"Every summer," Grandfather told him. "Every year."
36	Kenny loved the pond. It was part of a wetland area where
48	waterbirds lived. Dragonflies buzzed in the grass and wild
57	ducks swam.
59	But tonight Grandfather had bad news.
65	"Big changes are coming," Grandfather told Kenny.
72	"What kind of changes?"
76	"As more people come to live here, they'll need more houses
87	and more roads."
90	Kenny was surprised. "Where will they build them?"
98	he asked. 100

Comprehension Check

1. Why will more houses and roads be built? **Cause and Effect**

2. What did Kenny love about the pond? **Make Inferences**

	Words Read	–	Number of Errors	=	Words Correct Score
First Read		–		=	
Second Read		–		=	

© Macmillan/McGraw-Hill

CA R 1.6 Read aloud fluently and accurately and with appropriate intonation and expression.

Name _____

- **Photographs** are pictures that help you see what is described in the story.
- **Captions** are the words below a photograph or drawing. They tell what the picture is about.

Write a caption to go with each picture. Make each caption a complete sentence.

1.

_____

_____

2.

_____

_____

© Macmillan/McGraw-Hill

CA **R 2.1** Use titles, tables of contents, and chapter headings to locate information in expository text.

Tomás and the Library Lady
Grade 2/Unit 2
91

- Check the spelling of all plural nouns. Add **-es** to nouns that end in **s**, **sh**, **ch**, or **x**.
- When you write a letter, check that the greeting and the closing begin with capital letters.
- Use commas after the greeting and closing in the letter.

Find each mistake in the spelling of plural nouns, capitalization, and commas. Then rewrite the letter correctly on the lines below.

dear Ms. Green

Thank you for reading your storys to our class. We really liked the one about the three fox who live in three box. The story about the ponys who turned into mouses was great!

yours truly
Mr. Troy's class

_____

_____

_____

_____

CA LC 1.0 Written and Oral English Language Conventions

© Macmillan/McGraw-Hill

Name _____

A. There are six spelling mistakes in the paragraph below. Circle the misspelled words. Write the words correctly on the lines below.

My grandpa likes to tell stories. He tells me about things I did when I was a little babie. He remembers when wey went to the park together. He says that when I was a baby, I did not eet very much. Now I nead a lot of food to fill me up! Hee tells me about the first time I rode on a ponie. I did not want to get off. I hope my grandpa keeps telling me stories.

1. _____   2. _____   3. _____

4. _____   5. _____   6. _____

B. Writing

Write a family story. Use four words from the spelling list. Share and compare your story with a classmate's story.

_____

_____

_____

_____

© Macmillan/McGraw-Hill

LC 1.8 Spell basic short-vowel, long-vowel, *r*-controlled, and consonant-blend patterns correctly.

The long *i* sound can be spelled with the letters *i, ie, igh,* or *y*.

Choose a word from the box to complete each sentence.

why	climb	light	blind
tie	fly	high	pie

1. We like to _____ trees.

2. The street _____ shines in my window at night.

3. Dad likes apple _____ with raisins.

4. My friend has a seeing-eye dog. My friend is _____.

5. Mr. Simon wears a _____ with his suit.

6. The geese _____ south every year.

7. Ask if you want to know _____.

8. How _____ is that kite?

R 1.1 Recognize and use knowledge of spelling patterns (e.g., diphthongs, special vowel spellings) when reading.

© Macmillan/McGraw-Hill

Name _____

Read the sentences below. Match the lettered definitions with the underlined word in each sentence. Then write the letter of the correct definition on the line.

1. There are pine trees and oak trees in this <u>forest</u>. _____

2. <u>Heat</u> from the fire could hurt the trees. _____

3. The fire's hot <u>flames</u> burned some logs. _____

4. The firefighter wanted large <u>containers</u> of water to put out the fire. _____

5. Firefighters help children stay <u>safe</u>. _____

a. the hot, glowing part of a fire

b. things, such as boxes or jars, that hold goods

c. a large area of land covered with trees

d. great warmth or high temperature

e. unhurt or out of danger

© Macmillan/McGraw-Hill

- Some **proper nouns** name days of the week, months, and holidays.
- The name of each day, month, or holiday begins with a capital letter.

    <u>S</u>unday   <u>J</u>une   <u>F</u>ather's <u>D</u>ay

Choose the proper noun that names a day, month, or holiday. Write it correctly on the line below.

1. january
   winter
   vacation

   _____

2. flag
   vote
   president's day

   _____

3. holiday
   flowers
   mother's day

   _____

4. sunday
   day
   afternoon

   _____

5. fireworks
   summer
   july

   _____

6. vacation
   labor day
   weekend

   _____

7. september
   school
   teacher

   _____

8. thanksgiving
   fall
   family

   _____

© Macmillan/McGraw-Hill

CA **LC 1.6** Capitalize all proper nouns, words at the beginning of sentences and greetings, months and days of the week, and titles and initials of people.

Name _____

A **compound word** is made up of smaller words.

rain + bow = rainbow

pack	box	fall	plane

A. Put a word from the box with each word below to make a compound word. Write the compound word on the line.

I. water _____

2. mail _____

3. air _____

4. back _____

B. Circle the compound word. Then draw a line between the two smaller words.

5. wildfire   wild

6. nearer   nearby

7. firefighter   fighting

8. sunrise   sunny

9. times   daytime

R 1.0 Word Analysis, Fluency, and Systematic Vocabulary Development

Name _____

| light | lie | try | high | tie |
| wild | mind | sight | cry | dry |

A. Write the Words

Write the spelling words that have the long *i* sound spelled *i*.

1. _____   2. _____

Write the spelling words that have the long *i* sound spelled *ie*.

3. _____   4. _____

Write the spelling words that have the long *i* sound spelled *y*.

5. _____   6. _____   7. _____

Write the spelling words that have the long *i* sound spelled *igh*.

8. _____   9. _____   10. _____

B. Misfit Letter

An extra letter has been added to each spelling word below. Draw a line through the letter that does not belong. Write the word correctly on the line.

11. highe _____   12. miend _____

13. crye _____   14. tyie _____

15. wiled _____

© Macmillan/McGraw-Hill

CA **LC 1.8** Spell basic short-vowel, long-vowel, *r*-controlled, and consonant-blend patterns correctly.

© Macmillan/McGraw-Hill

As you read *Fighting the Fire*, fill in the Main Idea and Details Web.

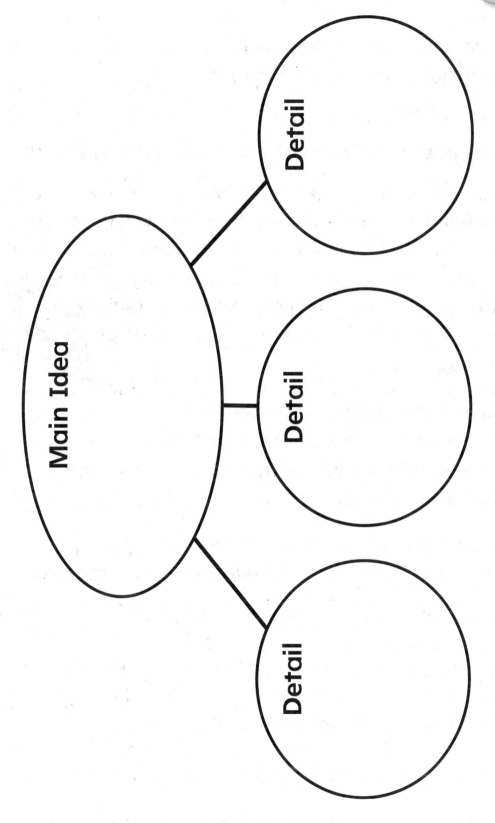

Main Idea

Detail

Detail

Detail

How does the information you wrote in this Main Idea and Details Web help you summarize *Fighting the Fire*?

> The **main idea** is the most important idea in a story. **Details** in the story tell more about the main idea.

A. Read the passage. Then circle the correct answer to the question.

When you think of foam, do you think of shampoo and shaving cream? Well, you're about to learn something new about foam. Firefighters use a special kind of foam to fight fires. They spray the foam through a hose. The foam covers the fire like a blanket. It blocks out the air the fire needs. Soon the fire is out.

1. What is the main idea of this paragraph?
   a. Firefighters use shampoo to put out fires.
   b. Fires need air to keep burning.
   c. Firefighters use special foam to put out fires.

B. Write yes if the detail tells about the main idea. Write no if the detail does not tell about the main idea.

2. Shampoo and shaving cream both make foam. _____

3. Special foam can block air from a fire. _____

4. Firefighters spray foam through a hose. _____

5. Firefighters learn new things about foam. _____

6. Special foam can cover a fire like a blanket. _____

© Macmillan/McGraw-Hill

CA R 2.0 Reading Comprehension

Name _____

A **word family** is a group of words that shares some of the
same sounds and letters. Knowing how to read one word in
a word family can help you to read other words in the same
family.

-ell family	*-eat* family
b +ell = bell	n +eat = neat

**Read the poems below. Circle all the words you find in
the *-ell* and *-eat* families.**

People call me Old Swell Dell.
All my sentences rhyme with yell.
On a hill is where I dwell,
With my lovely wife called Nell.
I have a bell I want to sell.
When you see it you will tell,
It's just as nice as Old Swell Dell.

_____

My name is Mr. Neat.
My sentences rhyme with heat.
Won't you take a seat.
I have a special treat.
Just listen to this beat!

© Macmillan/McGraw-Hill

Name _____

As I read, I will pay attention to the pronunciation of the vocabulary words.

	The alarm goes off.
4	The firefighters jump into the fire truck.
11	The lights on the truck turn on.
18	The siren blasts.
21	The firefighters race to the fire.
27	You gave 911 the address.
32	The truck can get to the fire fast.
40	The firefighters work to stop the **heat** and fire.
49	They save lives. 52

Comprehension Check

1. What is the first thing firefighters do when the alarm goes off? **Main Idea and Details**

2. What do the firefighters do when they get to the fire? **Main Idea and Details**

	Words Read	–	Number of Errors	=	Words Correct Score
First Read		–		=	
Second Read		–		=	

© Macmillan/McGraw-Hill

CA **R 1.6** Read aloud fluently and accurately and with appropriate intonation and expression.

A **title** is the name of a book or chapter. The **author** is who wrote the book. The **illustrator** is who made the book's pictures. The **table of contents** tells what is on the book's pages. The **title page** gives the book's title and the names of its author, illustrator, and publisher.

Read the title page and table of contents. Then find the correct answer in the column on the right to complete each sentence. Write its letter on the line.

Fire Trucks Old and New

by Lee Huong

Illustrated by Carol Sanchez

Published by Picture Book Press

Table of Contents

1. The First Fire Truck 3

2. How the Fire Truck Changed 12

3. Fire Trucks Around the World 21

4. The Newest Fire Trucks 30

1. The book's title is _____.

a. Picture Book Press

2. The book's author is _____.

b. four

3. The book's publisher is _____.

c. Fire Trucks Old and New

4. The book's illustrator is _____.

d. The Newest Fire Trucks

5. The book has _____ chapters.

e. Lee Huong

6. Chapter 4 is titled _____.

f. Carol Sanchez

© Macmillan/McGraw-Hill

CA **R 2.0** Reading Comprehension

Description Writing Frame

Summarize *Fighting the Fire*.
Use the Description Writing Frame below.

When a wildfire occurs, firefighters have an important job to do.

Firefighters work together. **Some** firefighters _____

_____

_____

_____

_____.

Other firefighters _____

_____

_____

_____

_____.

Firefighters help people, **too**. They _____

_____

_____

_____

_____.

© Macmillan/McGraw-Hill

Rewrite the completed summary on another sheet of paper. Keep it as a model for writing a summary of an article or selection using this text structure.

CA R 2.0 Reading Comprehension

Name _____

- The names of special people, places, or things begin with capital letters. The names of days of the week, months, and holidays begin with capital letters.
- An abbreviation begins with a capital letter and ends with a period.
- The greeting and the closing of a letter begin with capital letters. Use commas after the greeting and closing in the letter.

Find each mistake in capitalization and punctuation. Rewrite the letter correctly on the lines below.

dear dr moss

Thank you for seeing me on thursday. It was very nice of you to come to elwood hospital on thanksgiving. I hope you were still able to have a nice Holiday dinner.

yours truly

lisa

_____

_____

_____

_____

_____

_____

© Macmillan/McGraw-Hill

LC 1.6 Capitalize all proper nouns, words at the beginning of sentences and greetings, months and days of the week, and titles and initials of people.

Fighting the Fire • **Grade 2/Unit 2**   **105**

Name _____

A. There are five spelling mistakes in the report below. Circle the misspelled words. Write the words correctly on the lines below.

Our class took a trip to the zoo. We saw tame animals and wield animals. There was a baby kangaroo. He could jump highe. We did not miend getting splashed by the baby seal pups. We sat in the sun to get driy. We liked the newborn lion cubs the best.The zoo keeper told us not to trye to feed them. Their mother might get mad!

1. _____   2. _____   3. _____

4. _____   5. _____

B. Writing

Write a report about baby or adult animals. Use five words from the spelling list.

_____

_____

_____

_____

© Macmillan/McGraw-Hill

LC 1.8 Spell basic short-vowel, long-vowel, *r*-controlled, and consonant-blend patterns correctly.

Name _____

Search for the words from the box. Circle each word as you find it. Then write it in the correct list below.

coach	no	slow	toe	ago
toad	glow	goat	bow	foe

```
I  T  O  E  C  V  O  B  T
Y  J  P  T  H  C  P  X  O
A  G  O  S  K  O  E  B  A
U  G  W  L  J  A  N  O  D
E  L  Z  O  O  C  L  W  Z
O  O  X  W  R  H  C  M  J
F  W  P  D  A  G  O  A  T
```

I. words with the long *o* sound, as in *so*

_____

2. words with the long *o* sound, as in *Joe*

_____

3. words with the long *o* sound, as in *road*

_____

4. words with the long *o* sound, as in *grow*

_____

© Macmillan/McGraw-Hill

R 1.1 Recognize and use knowledge of spelling patterns (e.g., diphthongs, special vowel spellings) when reading.

**Read the story. Choose words from the box to complete
the sentences. Then write the answers on the lines.**

collectors	store	reward	clever	double	amount

My mom and dad love to fish. They enter fishing contests. They

have won many trophies. A trophy is something a fisher gets

to _____ him or her for catching the biggest fish.

Mom and Dad are _____ of fishing trophies.

When they first started, Mom and Dad only had a small

_____ of trophies. They worked hard and

became very _____ fishers. Soon they had

_____ the number of trophies. Each year, they

win more and more. They are making a new cabinet to

_____ all their trophies.

© Macmillan/McGraw-Hill

CA   R 1.0 Word Analysis, Fluency, and Systematic Vocabulary Development

Name _____

> • Add an apostrophe to most plural nouns to make them possessive.
>
> The <u>animals'</u> barn is red.
>
> • Add an apostrophe (') and **-s** to plural nouns that do not end in **s**.
>
> The <u>children's</u> trip to the farm was fun.

Underline the correct plural possessive noun in ().
Rewrite the sentence on the line below.

1. I found several (birds'/bird's) nests in our yard.

   _____

2. The (squirrel's/squirrels') tails are bushy.

   _____

3. The (bear's/bears') bodies are very big.

   _____

4. The (mice's/mices') noses twitch when they smell a cat.

   _____

5. The (dog's/dogs') owners are training their pets.

   _____

6. The (geeses'/geese's) beaks are wet.

   _____

© Macmillan/McGraw-Hill

Use *-s* or *-es* to make some words mean more than one.

Read each sentence. Then complete the sentence with one of the words from the list below it.

1. One of the worst _____ ever started last night.
   storm   storms   stormes

2. We heard loud _____ of thunder.
   crash   crashs   crashes

3. Huge _____ of rain fell from the sky.
   drop   drops   dropes

4. The rain covered the _____ and flooded the basement.
   steps   step   stepes

5. Our basement soon had six _____ of water in it!
   inch   inchs   inches

6. The next day, our _____ came to help.
   neighbor   neighbors   neighbores

7. They brought buckets and _____ to get the water up.
   mop   mops   mopes

8. Our neighbors were our _____.
   hero   heros   heroes

© Macmillan/McGraw-Hill

CA **R 1.5** Identify and correctly use regular plurals (e.g., *-s, -es, -ies*) and irregular plurals (e.g., *fly/flies, wife/wives*).

Name _____

| most | mow | goes | toast | foam |
| grow | told | bowl | toe | soap |

A.   Write the Words

Write the spelling words that have the long *o* sound spelled *o*.

1. _____   2. _____

Write the spelling words that have the long *o* sound spelled *oa*.

3. _____   4. _____   5. _____

Write the spelling words that have the long *o* sound spelled *ow*.

6. _____   7. _____   8. _____

Write the spelling words that have the long *o* sound spelled *oe*.

9. _____   10. _____

B.   Rhyme Time

Write the spelling word that rhymes with each of these words.

11. cold _____

12. hoes _____

13. rope _____

14. doe _____

15. roast _____

© Macmillan/McGraw-Hill

LC 1.8 Spell basic short-vowel, **long-vowel**, *r*-controlled, and
consonant-blend patterns correctly.

One Grain of Rice
Grade 2/Unit 2

111

Name _____

As you read *One Grain of Rice*, **fill in the Inference Chart.**

What I Read	What I Know

Inference

How does the information you wrote on this Inference Chart
help you understand *One Grain of Rice*?

© Macmillan/McGraw-Hill

CA   **R 2.0** Reading Comprehension

When you **make inferences**, you use what you already know and what you have read to figure out something about a story.

Read each set of sentences. Then answer each question to make an inference.

1. The man saw the cat up the tree. He ran and got a ladder.

   What is the man going to do? _____

2. The woman felt the boy's forehead. She looked at his throat and into his ears with a tool. She wrote something on a little piece of paper and gave it to the boy's father.

   Who is the woman? _____

3. Jared put on his cap. He picked up his glove and his bat.

   Where is Jared going? _____

4. The man has a stick with string on it. He puts something on the end of the string. Then he puts the end of the string in the water. He sits quietly, holding onto the stick. All of a sudden, the man pulls the string out of the water and smiles.

   What is on the end of the string? _____

© Macmillan/McGraw-Hill

Suffixes are word parts added to the ends of words to change their meanings.

-or means "a person who"

-less means "without"

Read each sentence. Underline the word that has the suffix *-or* or *-less*. Then write each word and its meaning.

1. The actor tried out for a part in the play.

_____

2. Many heroes are fearless.

_____

3. Pat thought getting her work done on time was hopeless.

_____

4. My uncle is an inventor.

_____

5. I would like to be a sailor and explore the oceans.

_____

6. The baby was toothless.

_____

© Macmillan/McGraw-Hill

CA **R 1.9** Know the meaning of simple prefixes and suffixes
(e.g., *over-*, *un-*, *-ing*, *-ly*).

As I read, I will pay attention to phrasing.

	If you travel south as far as you can go, you will reach
13	the South Pole. The South Pole is in Antarctica. Antarctica is
24	a continent covered with ice and snow. It is the coldest place
36	on Earth.
38	Strong winds blow across Antarctica. It does not rain.
47	It does not even snow very much.
54	A **vast** layer of ice, called an ice cap, covers the land. It is
68	more than a mile (about 2 kilometers) thick. The ice cap
78	extends into the sea.
82	The temperature in Antarctica is usually well below
90	32°F (0°C). Water freezes at this temperature. So ice and snow
101	don't melt in Antarctica.
105	Very few animals live in Antarctica. But many animals live
115	in the **oceans** around the ice cap for part of the year. 127

Comprehension Check

1. What is the weather like in Antarctica? **Main Idea and Details**

2. Why don't the ice and snow melt in Antarctica? **Make Inferences**

	Words Read	–	Number of Errors	=	Words Correct Score
First Read		–		=	
Second Read		–		=	

© Macmillan/McGraw-Hill

CA **R 1.6** Read aloud fluently and accurately and with appropriate
intonation and expression.

A. Suppose you have to write a paper about a community worker who shows strength and courage. Answer each question below.

1. Circle the topic that best fits the assignment.

actors   painters   police officers

2. Which reference material would be the best one to use to find information about your topic?

storybook   dictionary   nonfiction book

3. Why is your choice the best reference material to use for this topic?

_____

_____

_____

_____

_____

B. Use these section headings to answer the questions:

What Police Do	Where Police Work	How Police Learn the Job

4. In which section would you find out what kind of school you need to attend to become a police officer?

_____

5. Which section would tell what police do during their workday?

_____

CA **R 2.1** Use titles, tables of contents, and chapter headings to locate information in expository text.

© Macmillan/McGraw-Hill

Name _____

- Add an apostrophe and **-s** to make a singular noun possessive.

- Add an apostrophe to make most plural nouns possessive.

Circle each mistake. Rewrite the passage correctly on the lines below.

A frogs eggs are called egg spawn. The eggs shells protect the egg spawn. Soon the eggs hatch. Tadpoles come out. The new tadpoles tails are very long. Did you know that tadpoles eat frogs eggs?

_____

_____

_____

_____

_____

_____

© Macmillan/McGraw-Hill

Name _____

A. There are five spelling mistakes in the paragraph below. Circle the misspelled words. Write the words correctly on the lines below.

When I groe up, I want to play baseball like my brother. He gois to practice every day. He tolde me that he works hard to be a good player. He has never missed a game. Once he even played with a broken tow. What he loves moast about baseball is that it helps keep him in shape.

1. _____   2. _____   3. _____

4. _____   5. _____

B. Writing

What sport or activity keeps
you in good shape? Write about it.
Use five spelling words from your list.

_____

_____

_____

_____

CA **LC 1.8** Spell basic short-vowel, long-vowel, *r*-controlled, and consonant-blend patterns correctly.

© Macmillan/McGraw-Hill

Name _____

Listen to the long *u* sound as you say each of these words.

mule   **use**   **tune**

**A. Choose the word from the box that names each picture.
Careful! You will not use all the words in the box.**

rug	tuba	June	use
cube	cub	cute	mule

1. _____

2. _____

3. _____

4. _____

**B. Find the words from the box with the long *u* sound that
do not name a picture. Then write a sentence for each
word on the lines below.**

5. _____

6. _____

© Macmillan/McGraw-Hill

CA **R 1.1** Recognize and use knowledge of spelling patterns
(e.g., diphthongs, special vowel spellings) when reading.

African-American Inventors
Grade 2/Unit 2

119

Name _____

A. Write a word from the box to complete each sentence.

powerful	allowed	products
design	instrument	invented

1. The city _____ thousands of people to gather in the park for a concert.

2. The new medical _____ helped the doctors find the problem.

3. The _____ beam of light could be seen for miles.

4. Many new _____ are for sale every year.

5. The _____ for the new building was unlike any other building's in town.

6. My hero is the person who _____ peanut butter!

B. Write two sentences that each use one word from the box.

7. _____

8. _____

© Macmillan/McGraw-Hill

Name _____

- Add apostrophe (') and **-s** to a singular noun to make it possessive.

  The <u>girl's</u> towel is wet.

- Add an apostrophe to make most plural nouns possessive.

  Several <u>swimmers'</u> caps are white.

Circle the mistake in each sentence. Then write the possessive noun correctly on the line below.

1. The girls goggles are on their faces.

_____

2. The boys suit is red.

_____

3. The coachs whistle is around her neck.

_____

4. All three swimmers laps are very strong.

_____

5. The fans applause is loud.

_____

© Macmillan/McGraw-Hill

Name _____

Before adding **-ing** to some verbs with short vowels, double the final consonant.

A. Add -ing to each word. Then use each new word in a sentence.

1. run _____

_____

2. hop _____

_____

3. get _____

_____

B. Add -ed to each word. Then use each new word in a sentence.

4. lock _____

_____

5. help _____

_____

6. jump _____

_____

© Macmillan/McGraw-Hill

CA **R 1.0** Word Analysis, Fluency, and Systematic Vocabulary Development

Name _____

| flute | tune | dune | use | June |
| mule | duke | bugle | music | fuse |

A. Word Sort

Look at the spelling words in the box. Write the spelling words that have the long *u* sound spelled *u*.

1. _____   2. _____

Write the spelling words that have the long *u* sound spelled *u_e*.

3. _____   4. _____   5. _____

6. _____   7. _____   8. _____

9. _____   10. _____

B. Puzzle

Solve the puzzle. Circle the five hidden spelling words.

```
e   u   m   u   l   e   z
i   f   l   u   t   e   s
u   s   e   f   n   k   g
e   c   n   t   u   n   e
y   d   u   n   e   l   m
```

© Macmillan/McGraw-Hill

LC 1.8 Spell basic short-vowel, long-vowel, *r*-controlled, and
consonant-blend patterns correctly.

African-American Inventors   123
Grade 2/Unit 2

As you read *African-American Inventors,* **fill in the Compare and Contrast Charts.**

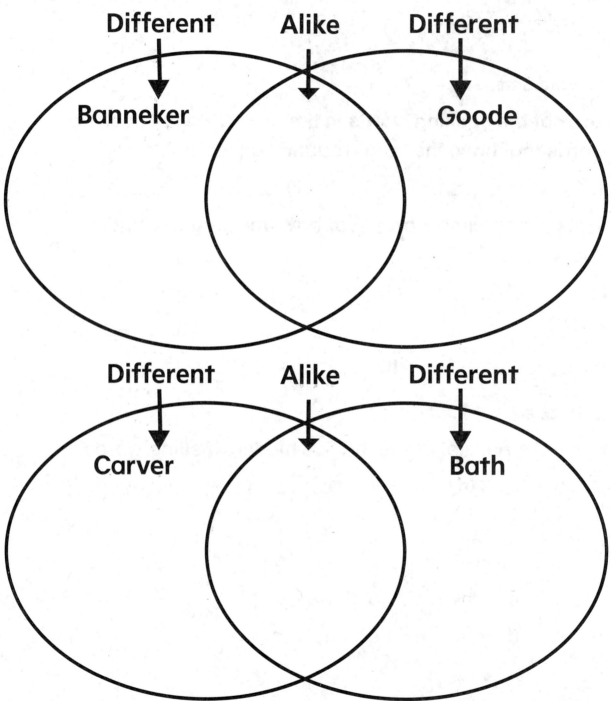

Different   Alike   Different

Banneker   Goode

Different   Alike   Different

Carver   Bath

How does the information you wrote in this Compare and Contrast Charts help you to better understand *African-American Inventors*?

© Macmillan/McGraw-Hill

CA R 2.0 Reading Comprehension

When you **compare,** you tell how two or more things are alike.

When you **contrast,** you tell how two or more things are different.

Read the passage. Then answer the questions below.

    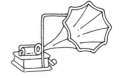

Alexander Graham Bell was an inventor. He was born in Scotland in 1849. Alexander Graham Bell invented the telephone.

Thomas Edison was an inventor. He was born in America in 1849. Thomas Edison invented the light bulb, movie camera, and phonograph.

I. How were Alexander Graham Bell and Thomas Edison alike?

_____

_____

_____

2. How were Alexander Graham Bell and Thomas Edison different?

_____

_____

_____

_____

© Macmillan/McGraw-Hill

A **suffix** is a word part added to the end of a base word.
It changes the meaning of the base word.

**A. Add –*ful* and –*less* to each word. Then write what
each new word means.**

1. cheer _____   _____

2. cheer _____   _____

3. harm _____   _____

4. harm _____   _____

5. care _____   _____

6. care _____   _____

7. power _____   _____

8. power _____   _____

**B. Pick two words you wrote above. Then use each word
in a sentence.**

9. _____

10. _____

© Macmillan/McGraw-Hill

CA **R 1.9** Know the meaning of simple prefixes and **suffixes**
(e.g., *over-, un-, -ing, -ly*).

**As I read, I will pay attention to the pronunciation
of the vocabulary words.**

9	In the 1880s, Karl Benz and Gottlieb Daimler built the first cars that used gasoline. These looked more like the cars
20	we drive today. So, in a way, Benz and Daimler were the first
33	to **invent** modern cars.
37	The first cars cost too much for most people to buy. Henry Ford
50	was an American car maker. He started making cars on an
61	assembly line. On an assembly line each worker does only one
72	job. This is a much faster, cheaper way of making things. Today,
84	many cars and other **products** are made this way in factories.
95	Before assembly lines, it took Ford's workers more than
104	12 hours to make one car. After, it took only 90 minutes.
114	By the 1920s, Ford was making one car every 43 seconds!
123	Because they were cheap to make, Ford's cars were cheap
133	to buy. This **allowed** more people to own a car. 143

Comprehension Check

1. How were cars different after Ford's assembly line? **Compare
and Contrast**

2. Do you think the assembly line changed businesses other than
auto making? **Draw Conclusions**

	Words Read	−	Number of Errors	=	Words Correct Score
First Read		−		=	
Second Read		−		=	

© Macmillan/McGraw-Hill

R 1.6 Read aloud fluently and accurately and with appropriate intonation
and expression.

Name _____

A **time line** shows when important things happened.

Use the time line to answer the questions.

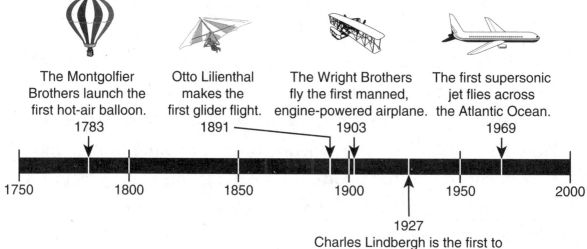

The Montgolfier
Brothers launch the
first hot-air balloon.
1783

Otto Lilienthal
makes the
first glider flight.
1891

The Wright Brothers
fly the first manned,
engine-powered airplane.
1903

The first supersonic
jet flies across
the Atlantic Ocean.
1969

1750   1800   1850   1900   1950   2000

1927
Charles Lindbergh is the first to
fly across the Atlantic Ocean by himself.

1. What happened in 1783? _____

_____

2. When did Lindbergh cross the Atlantic Ocean? _____

3. What happened 24 years before Lindbergh's flight? _____

_____

_____

4. How many years after Lilienthal's glider flight did the Wright

Brothers fly? _____

© Macmillan/McGraw-Hill

CA **R 2.7** Interpret information from diagrams, charts, and graphs.

Name _____

- Add an apostrophe and **-s** to make a singular noun possessive.

- Add an apostrophe to make most plural nouns possessive.

- Do not add an apostrophe to form a plural noun.

- Use commas to separate three or more words in a series.

Find each mistake with plurals, possessives, and commas. Rewrite the passage correctly on the lines below.

At Ellas school, students choices for sports are tennis soccer and basketball. Ellas' mom and dad think she should play soccer. Her brothers favorite sport is basketball. Ella loves all sport's!

_____

_____

_____

_____

© Macmillan/McGraw-Hill

A. There are five spelling mistakes in the list of rules below. Circle the misspelled words. Write the words correctly on the lines below.

Rules for Music Class

1. Do not uise instruments without asking the teacher.

2. Tuune your instrument before class begins.

3. Make sure no one will trip on your buggle.

4. Keep your fluit in the case unless you are playing it.

5. Put all of the musec books in a neat stack before you leave.

1. _____   2. _____   3. _____

4. _____   5. _____

B. Writing

Write about other school rules that are important to follow. Use five spelling words from your list.

_____

_____

_____

_____

© Macmillan/McGraw-Hill

CA **LC 1.8** Spell basic short-vowel, long-vowel, *r*-controlled, and consonant-blend patterns correctly.

Name _____

The letters **er**, **ir**, and **ur** can sometimes stand for the same sounds.

Listen for the middle sounds as you say these words.

herd   **fir**st   **bur**n

A. Read the words in the box below. Then circle the letters in each word that stand for the vowel sound.

turn   herd   curl   bird   term   girl

B. Write the words from the box that have the same vowel sound and spelling as the name of the picture.

-er words	**-ir** words	**-ur** words
 fern	 shirt	 nurse
1. _____	3. _____	5. _____
2. _____	4. _____	6. _____

© Macmillan/McGraw-Hill

CA **R 1.1** Recognize and use knowledge of spelling patterns (e.g., diphthongs, special vowel spellings) when reading.

The Alvin Ailey Kids
Grade 2/Unit 3   131

Name _____

A. Write the word from the box to complete each sentence.

| remember | perform | effort | proud | mood |

1. Charlene's hard work and _____ really paid off.

2. The school band will _____ next week.

3. Ruthann was _____ to be singing in the school play.

4. Nathan can _____ his lines for the play.

5. Pizza for lunch always puts me in a good _____.

B. Choose two words from the box. Write a sentence for each word on the lines below.

6. _____

7. _____

© Macmillan/McGraw-Hill

CA   R 1.0 Word Analysis, Fluency, and Systematic Vocabulary Development

Name _____

> • Some action verbs show actions you can see.
>
>   Habib <u>reads</u> a book.
>
> • Some action verbs tell about actions that are hard to see.
>
>   Habib <u>enjoys</u> books about animals.

Read each sentence. Underline the action verb. Then write another sentence using that same verb.

1. The three bears walk in the woods.

   _____

2. Goldilocks likes the porridge.

   _____

3. Goldilocks sits in Baby Bear's chair.

   _____

4. She breaks the chair.

   _____

5. Goldilocks feels tired.

   _____

6. The bears come home.

   _____

7. The bears find Goldilocks asleep.

   _____

8. They chase Goldilocks away.

   _____

© Macmillan/McGraw-Hill

LC 1.3 Identify and correctly use various parts of speech, including nouns and verbs, in writing and speaking.

The Alvin Ailey Kids **133**
Grade 2/Unit 3

You can add the endings **-er** and **-est** to make comparisons.

The ending **-er** means "more than."

The ending **-est** means "most."

Add -er or -est to the words in the box to complete each sentence.

bright	fast	loud	tall

The lights were low. Then the lights got _____.

My class came onto the stage. The short children were in the

first row. The _____ ones were in the next row.

The _____ ones of all were in the last row. The

children began to dance. First, they danced slowly. Then they

danced _____. At the end, everyone cheered for us.

My mom cheered _____ than anyone else.

CA R **1.0** Word Analysis, Fluency, and Systematic Vocabulary
Development

© Macmillan/McGraw-Hill

Name _____

term	hurt	first	herd	stir
skirt	clerk	churn	burst	turn

A. Word Sort

Look at the spelling words in the box. Match each word
with a spelling pattern.

er   1. _____   2. _____   3. _____

ir   4. _____   5. _____   6. _____

ur   7. _____   8. _____   9. _____

10. _____

B. Misfit Letter

An extra letter has been added to each spelling word
below. Draw a line through the letter that does not
belong. Write the word correctly on the line.

11. stier _____

12. hierd _____

13. clierk _____

14. huert _____

15. cheurn _____

© Macmillan/McGraw-Hill

LC 1.8 Spell basic short-vowel, long-vowel, *r*-controlled, and
consonant-blend patterns correctly.

The Alvin Ailey Kids   135
Grade 2/Unit 3

Name _____

As you read *The Alvin Ailey Kids: Dancing As a Team*,
fill in the Summarize Chart.

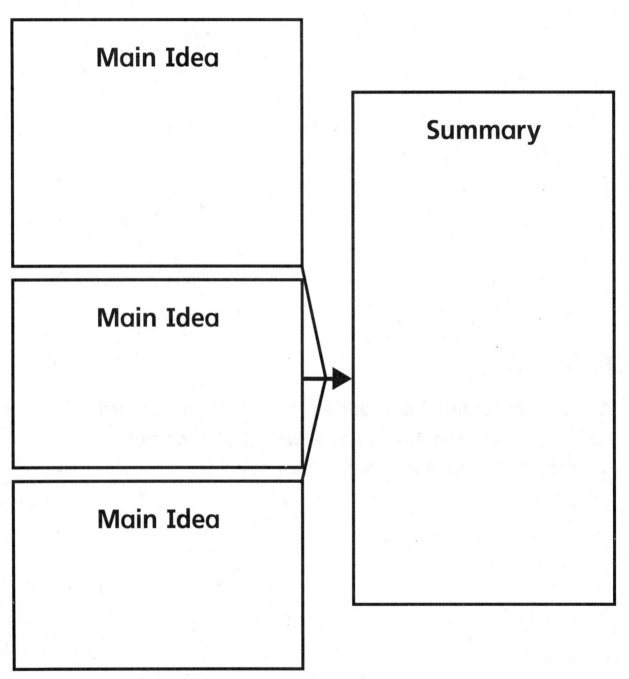

How does the information you wrote in this Summarize Chart help
you to better understand *The Alvin Ailey Kids: Dancing As a Team*?

CA   R 2.0 Reading Comprehension

© Macmillan/McGraw-Hill

Name _____

When you **summarize** a story, you tell the main ideas
and details in your own words. The **main idea** is the
most important idea in a story. **Details** in the story tell
more information about the main idea.

**Read each story. Then underline the sentence that
summarizes each passage.**

1. The toy Noah liked best was a kazoo. He also played
   with toy flutes and horns. Now he plays the recorder.
   When Noah is bigger and stronger, he wants to try the
   tuba. Right now a tuba is bigger than he is!
   a. Noah likes to play music.
   b. Noah plays the kazoo.
   c. Noah is too small to play the tuba.

2. The school marching band was ready. Their instruments were
   tuned. Their uniforms were neat and clean. At halftime the band
   lined up. When they marched out onto the field, everyone cheered.
   a. The marching band tuned their instruments.
   b. The marching band wore neat and clean uniforms.
   c. The marching band performs at halftime.

3. Wendy has an older sister named Jane. They both go to ballet
   class after school. Eve has a younger sister named Lara. They
   go to tap class. The girls' classes are in the same dance school.
   In the spring they will all perform in the dance concert.
   a. All the girls have sisters.
   b. All the girls like to dance.
   c. The dance concert is in the spring.

© Macmillan/McGraw-Hill

Look for the definition of words in the **dictionary**.
Use a **thesaurus** to find antonyms and synonyms.

Dictionary	Thesaurus
applaud (uh-**plawd**) *verb* To show that you like something by clapping your hands. **chorus** (**kor**-uhss) *noun* A group of people who sing or dance together.	**applaud** *synonyms*: clap, appreciate *antonyms*: boo, hiss, jeer **chorus** *synonyms*: choir, glee club *antonyms*: star, soloist

Read each sentence. Use the dictionary and thesaurus entries above to find an antonym for the word in dark print. Then write the new word on the line.

1. We were excited to see the show. We began to **boo** as the

   performers came on stage. _____

2. The **soloist** stood along the back of the stage.

   _____

3. The **chorus** stood at the front of the stage. _____

4. When the beautiful song ended, we did not hear anyone

   applaud. _____

CA R 1.7 Understand and explain common antonyms and synonyms.

© Macmillan/McGraw-Hill

As I read, I will pay attention to my expression.

	When Nan was eight, she joined a sports school
9	in the Chinese city of Beijing (bay-JING). Only the
17	best child athletes in the country live and train at
27	special schools like this one.
32	Training to be a gymnast is hard work. Children
41	begin with stretches at 6:30 in the morning! Next,
49	they go into classrooms. That is where they are
58	taught reading, math, and other lessons until
65	lunchtime. There is a lot to **remember**.
72	After lunch, the younger students take a nap.
80	Then training goes on until dinnertime. Sometimes
87	the children **perform** the same exercise for an hour.
96	They only stop when they do it right. 104

Comprehension Check

1. What did Nan do when she was eight? **Main Idea and Details**

2. When does the training day begin at Nan's school? **Main Idea and Details**

	Words Read	–	Number of Errors	=	Words Correct Score
First Read		–		=	
Second Read		–		=	

© Macmillan/McGraw-Hill

CA **R 1.6** Read aloud fluently and accurately and with appropriate intonation and expression.

Alliteration is the repeated use of the same beginning sound in a group of words.

Alice sells **a**pples in **A**tlanta.

Rhythmic patterns are sounds and words that repeat to make a rhythm.

Mary had a little lamb, little lamb, little lamb.

Read the lyrics to this American folk song. Then follow the directions.

Sunny valley, sunny valley,

Sunny valley low.

When you're in that sunny valley,

Sing it soft and slow.

Stormy ocean, stormy ocean,

Stormy ocean wide.

When you're on that stormy ocean,

There's no place you can hide.

1. Circle the group of words in these lyrics that shows alliteration.

2. Underline two groups of words in these lyrics that repeat to give a certain rhythm.

© Macmillan/McGraw-Hill

CA R 2.0 Reading Comprehension

Name _____

- An abbreviation is a short way of writing a word. It starts with a capital letter and ends with a period.

- An action verb is a part of speech that tells what someone or something is doing.

Read the paragraph and find the mistakes in abbreviations and action verbs. Rewrite the passage correctly on the lines below.

dr. Chen is a childrens doctor. He buys lots of books for the waiting room. mrs Gomez, the nurse, enjoying reading to the children when she has time. "mr Poppleton" is everyone's favorite story.

_____

_____

_____

_____

_____

© Macmillan/McGraw-Hill

A. There are five spelling mistakes in the paragraph below. Circle the misspelled words. Write the words correctly on the lines below.

Animals have many different needs. Jason knows this from helping on his father's ranch. It is Jason's tirn to help with the cattle. There is a large hurd. They all need to stay together. Jason also needs to make sure that none of the cattle gets hert. Jason needs to stur a special medicine into the food of one cow that is sick. This is a big job. It takes a berst of energy for Jason to take care of the whole herd.

1. _____   2. _____   3. _____

4. _____   5. _____

Writing

B. Write a paragraph about the needs of one of your favorite animals. Use five words from your spelling list.

_____

_____

_____

_____

CA **LC 1.8** Spell basic short-vowel, long-vowel, *r*-controlled, and consonant-blend patterns correctly.

© Macmillan/McGraw-Hill

Name _____

When the letter *r* follows a vowel, the vowel usually changes its sound. The vowel sound is no longer short or long. Listen to the vowel sounds as you say each word.

n**ear**   d**eer**   h**ere**   h**er**

Read each word. Then circle the word that rhymes with it. (Hint: The ending sounds that rhyme may *not* be spelled the same.)

I. hear

pair   where   dear

2. steer

clean   deer   care

3. stern

stare   fern   bear

4. ear

swear   peer   far

5. germ

term   wear   dear

6. jeer

gear   jar   dare

7. here

there   her   fear

8. nerve

deer   near   serve

© Macmillan/McGraw-Hill

CA **R 1.1** Recognize and use knowledge of spelling patterns (e.g., diphthongs, special vowel spellings) when reading.

Abuelo and the Three Bears
Grade 2/Unit 3   143

Name _____

Read the story. Choose words from the box to complete the sentences. Then write the answers on the lines.

medium	stubborn	noticed	cozy	arrive	argue

You know the story of the three little pigs. You must have

_____ how mean the big, bad wolf was. The pigs

wanted to relax in their warm, _____ houses. But

the wolf was _____ . He had to have his way.

He blew down the first pig's house with ease. He used a

_____ amount of force for the second house. The

two pigs ran to the house of the third pig. They were able to

_____ just before the wolf caught them. The third

pig tried to _____ with the wolf and get him to

leave. But you know the story. That mean wolf came to a bad end.

CA **R 1.0** Word Analysis, Fluency, and Systematic Vocabulary Development

© Macmillan/McGraw-Hill

- A present-tense verb must agree with its subject.
- Add **-s** to most verbs if the subject is singular. Add **-es** to verbs that end with **s**, **ch**, **sh**, **x**, or **z**.

  The car <u>stops</u> for the red light.

- Do not add **-s** or **-es** if the subject is plural.

  The children <u>cross</u> the street.

Draw a line under the correct present-tense verb in ( ). Then write another sentence using the same verb on the line below.

1. The woman (push, pushes) the swing gently.

   _____

2. The child (giggles, giggle).

   _____

3. The children (goes, go) down the slide one at a time.

   _____

4. Two boys (ride, rides) their bikes around the park.

   _____

5. One boy (wear, wears) a red helmet to stay safe.

   _____

6. The other (have, has) a green helmet on his head.

   _____

CA **LC 1.3** Identify and correctly use various parts of speech, including
nouns and verbs, in writing and speaking.

Abuelo and the Three Bears
Grade 2/Unit 3
145

Name _____

Some words have **silent letters**.

know   **gn**ome   si**gn**   **w**rist   lim**b**

A. Choose two words from the word box that have the same silent letter as each of the words below. Write the words on the line.

knots lamb wrist gnaw knows wrong comb gnash

1. wrap _____ _____   **3.** gnat _____ _____

2. climb _____ _____   **4.** knife _____ _____

B. Complete each sentence with a word from the word box.

5. In an old story, a mouse _____ how to save a lion.

6. Hunters trap a lion with strong ropes and tight _____.

7. The lion thinks the mouse is too small to help, but he is _____.

8. The mouse is able to _____ through the ropes with its sharp teeth.

© Macmillan/McGraw-Hill

CA R 1.1 Recognize and use knowledge of spelling patterns (e.g., diphthongs, special vowel spellings) when reading.

Name _____

| near | where | deer | verb | perch |
| ear | steer | here | dear | cheer |

A. Word Sort

Look at the spelling words in the box. Write the spelling words that have the *er* spelling pattern.

1. _____   2. _____

Write the spelling words that have the *eer* spelling pattern.

3. _____   4. _____   5. _____

Write the spelling words that have the *ere* spelling pattern.

6. _____   7. _____

Write the spelling words that have the *ear* spelling pattern.

8. _____   9. _____   10. _____

B. Find the Pattern

Read each group of words. Circle the word that does not fit the pattern.

11. near, ear, deer

12. here, verb, where

13. perch, steer, queer

14. where, dear, near

15. deer, perch, verb

LC 1.8 Spell basic short-vowel, long-vowel, r-controlled, and consonant-blend patterns correctly.

Abuelo and the Three Bears
Grade 2/Unit 3   147

Name _____

As you read *Abuelo and The Three Bears*, fill in the Summarizing Chart.

Beginning

Middle

Summary

End

© Macmillan/McGraw-Hill

CA R 2.0 Reading Comprehension

A **summary** is a short account of a story. It gives the main ideas. It tells briefly what happened in the beginning, middle, and end.

Read the story. Then circle the better summary.

Once there was a little girl who lived near a big forest. Every day, her mother would tell her never to go into the forest. "If you do," she would say, "the Gunniwolf might get you."

One day the little girl saw some beautiful flowers growing at the edge of the woods. The little girl decided to pick them. Deeper into the forest, she saw some more. She decided to pick them, too. All the while, she sang a sweet song to herself.

Suddenly up rose the Gunniwolf. "Little girl, sing that sweet song again!" he demanded. She sang. Soon the Gunniwolf fell fast asleep.

The little girl raced out of the forest. And she has never gone into the forest again.

I. A mother told her daughter never to go into the nearby forest. The little girl went into the forest to pick flowers. She sang while she picked. The Gunniwolf saw her. He asked her to sing again, and he fell asleep. She never went into the forest again.

2. The Gunniwolf lived in the forest. He saw a little girl picking flowers. He asked her to sing. He liked her song very much. He knew that she lived in a little house. Anyone who went into the forest was very foolish indeed.

© Macmillan/McGraw-Hill

An **idiom** is a group of words that has a meaning that is different from the meanings of each individual word.

Idiom: My mom said "**Hold your horses**," when Nick begged to go to the park.

Meaning: Mom wants Nick to be patient.

completely   respect   change   met up with

trouble   did not work out   be very happy   in a bad mood

Read each sentence. Look at the idiom in dark type. Pick the meaning of the idiom from the box. Write the meaning on the line.

1. Anansi the tricky spider wanted to **turn over a new leaf**.

_____

2. He wanted the other animals to **look up to** him.

_____

3. He thought he would **feel like a million** if others liked him.

_____

4. But his plans to change **fell through**.

_____

5. He **ran across** a friend, and he just had to trick him.

_____

© Macmillan/McGraw-Hill

CA R 1.0 Word Analysis, Fluency, and Systematic Vocabulary Development

As I read, I will pay attention to expression and intonation.

	Many spacecraft have visited the moon, and 12
8	astronauts have walked on the lunar surface. Neil
16	Armstrong and Edwin "Buzz" Aldrin were the first people
25	to walk on the moon. The most famous thing Armstrong
35	left behind was his footprint! There is no air, wind, or
46	rain on the moon, so the footprint is still visible. It is there
59	to be discovered by another astronaut.
65	Some astronauts are now living on the International
73	Space Station. The station is a huge research center. One
83	day it may also be a launching pad to new places in space.
96	Maybe one day you will become an astronaut or live on
107	a space station. Right now, very few people can be called
118	star sailors! 120

Comprehension Check

1. Who were the first people to walk on the moon? **Main Idea and Details**

2. How can you summarize this passage? **Summarize**

	Words Read	–	Number of Errors	=	Words Correct Score
First Read		–		=	
Second Read		–		=	

© Macmillan/McGraw-Hill

CA R 1.6 Read aloud fluently and accurately and with appropriate intonation and expression.

Abuelo and the Three Bears
Grade 2/Unit 3   151

> Words that rhyme have the same ending sound, with
> different beginning sounds.
>
> Examples: tall/wall; pound/ground

**Read the poem. Circle the words that rhyme. Then finish
the poem.**

> When clouds make pictures in the sky,
> Fairy tales go floating by.
> I see three bears.
> I see three pigs.
> I see a boy who learns to fly.

When clouds make pictures in the sky,

Fairy tales go floating by.

1. I see _____

2. I see _____

3. I see _____

When clouds make pictures in the sky,

Fairy tales go floating by.

4. I see _____

5. I see _____

6. I see _____

© Macmillan/McGraw-Hill

CA R 2.0 Reading Comprehension

Name _____

- A present-tense verb must agree with its subject.
- Add **-s** or **-es** if the verb is singular.
- Use commas to separate three or more words in a series.

Find mistakes in the paragraph. Then rewrite the paragraph correctly on the lines below.

Each year a firefighter police officer or emergency worker come to our school. The firefighter teach us about stop drop and roll. The police officer tell us not to talks to strangers. We learns about 911 and giving our name number and address in an emergency.

_____

_____

_____

_____

_____

LC 1.3 Identify and correctly use various parts of speech, including nouns and verbs, in writing and speaking.

Abuelo and the Three Bears
Grade 2/Unit 3   153

A. There are six spelling mistakes in the paragraph below. Circle the misspelled words. Write the words correctly on the lines below.

My mom is an artist. She has a studio wheer she works every day. We live nere the woods so my mom draws lots of animals. One day she drew a der that she saw right outside her window. A fisherman lives next door, so my mom painted a picture of a peerch for him. My mom painted a picture of a cool race car for me. I let out a big chear. I have it hanging heer in my bedroom. Now I want to be an artist too!

I. _____ 2. _____ 3. _____

4. _____ 5. _____ 6. _____

B. Writing

Write about what you would draw or paint if you were an artist. Use four words from your spelling list.

_____

_____

_____

© Macmillan/McGraw-Hill

CA **LC 1.8** Spell basic short-vowel, long-vowel, *r*-controlled, and consonant-blend patterns correctly.

The vowel sound you hear in these words is followed by the **r** sound. The vowel sound is changed by the **r** that follows it.

You can hear the **ar** sound in **car** and **art**.

Write a word from the box to complete each sentence.

farm	arm	card	bark	dark

1. I hurt my right _____ playing baseball.

2. We shut off all the lights so the room was completely

_____.

3. I heard the neighbor's dog _____ all night.

4. My grandmother sent me a _____ to wish me a happy birthday.

5. Laura visits her grandfather's _____ to see the cows, horses, and pigs.

R 1.1 Recognize and use knowledge of spelling patterns (e.g., diphthongs, special vowel spellings) when reading.

CA

Music of the Stone Age
Grade 2/Unit 3

155

© Macmillan/McGraw-Hill

Name _____

A. Read each sentence. Choose a word from the box that has almost the same meaning as the underlined word or words. Then write the word on the line.

| talent | treasures | impossible | pleasant |

I. Reading a long book in just a few minutes is <u>not possible</u>.

_____

2. A warm breeze and sunny sky makes this an <u>enjoyable</u> day.

_____

3. Your <u>amazing gift</u> for painting helped you to win the art contest.

_____

4. A pirate would love to have this box of <u>very valuable things</u>.

_____

B. Write a new sentence using two of the words from the box.

5. _____

_____

© Macmillan/McGraw-Hill

CA R 1.0 Word Analysis, Fluency, and Systematic Vocabulary Development

Name _____

- If a verb ends with one consonant, double the consonant and add **-ed**.

    The car <u>stopped</u> at the red light.
- If a verb ends with **e**, drop the **e** and add **-ed**.

    The car <u>moved</u> at the green light.

Change each present-tense verb to past tense. Then use the verb in a sentence. Write the sentence on the line.

1. tap _____

_____

2. bake _____

_____

3. smile _____

_____

4. trim _____

_____

5. love _____

_____

© Macmillan/McGraw-Hill

LC 1.3 Identify and correctly use various parts of speech, including
nouns and verbs, in writing and speaking.

Music of the Stone Age
Grade 2/Unit 3   157

The letters **-ed** can be added to the end of a verb to change its tense.

If a word ends in silent **e**, drop the **e** before adding **-ed**.

use − e + ed = used

**Add -ed to the end of each word. Write the new word.
Then use the word in a sentence.**

1. wipe _____

_____

2. dance _____

_____

3. tune _____

_____

4. like _____

_____

5. joke _____

_____

6. raise _____

_____

© Macmillan/McGraw-Hill

CA **R 1.0** Word Analysis, Fluency, and Systematic Vocabulary Development

Name _____

A. There are five spelling mistakes in the sentences below. Circle the misspelled words. Write the words correctly on the lines below.

1. These ar my favorite jeans.

2. I like to staret my homework right after school.

3. Sue and Jeff take their dog to the parke every day.

4. I thought the math test was very hared.

5. The ending was the best parrt of the movie.

1. _____   2. _____   3. _____

4. _____   5. _____

B. Circle the Word

Circle the words with *ar*.

dark	short	sort	storm	far
horse	park	large	hard	corn

© Macmillan/McGraw-Hill

LC 1.8 Spell basic short-vowel, long-vowel, *r*-controlled, and consonant-blend patterns correctly.

Music of the Stone Age
Grade 2/Unit 3   159

As you read *Music of the Stone Age*, fill in the Author's Purpose Chart.

Clue	Clue

Author's Purpose

How does the information you wrote in this Author's Purpose Chart help you to better understand *Music of the Stone Age*?

© Macmillan/McGraw-Hill

One way to summarize a selection is to think about the **author's purpose**. The author's purpose is the writer's reason for writing.

Read each story. Then write the author's purpose on the lines.

1. Giraffes live in dry woodland areas. Their very long necks help them reach the leaves at the tops of trees. If there are no more leaves, giraffes reach food by kneeling down.

_____

_____

2. When she was a little girl, Ella loved to go to the beach. She loved to look at the sea plants and animals. She wrote many reports about the sea at school. When Ella grew up, she became a sea scientist.

_____

_____

3. There is too much litter in our town. The trash on the road smells bad. It can also hurt our animals if they eat it by accident. Let's all try harder to clean up our trash.

_____

_____

© Macmillan/McGraw-Hill

Some words can have more than one meaning. They are called **multiple-meaning words**. You can look at the other words in the sentence to help you decide which meaning fits best in the sentence.

I hit the baseball with a **bat**.

The **bat** flew out of the cave at night.

Read each sentence. Then write the meaning of the underlined word.

1. You can <u>lie</u> here to take a nap.

_____

2. I try to tell the truth and never <u>lie</u>.

_____

3. Cassie will start third grade next <u>fall</u>.

_____

4. Be careful not to slip and <u>fall</u> on the ice.

_____

5. I have a cast on my <u>right</u> arm.

_____

6. You chose the <u>right</u> answer.

_____

© Macmillan/McGraw-Hill

CA R 1.10 Identify simple multiple-meaning words.

As I read, I will pay attention to the pronunciation of the vocabulary word.

	Cats have been around for thousands of years. Long ago,
10	cats were more than house pets. People thought that they
20	had special powers. Artists painted pictures of cats. They also
30	created sculptures of cats.
34	Today, we can see paintings and sculptures of cats in museums.
45	Thousands of years ago in ancient Egypt, cats were honored
55	animals. The Egyptians loved cats so much that one of their
66	gods had the head of a cat. People who hurt cats were punished.
79	Cats were thought of as **treasures**.
85	The ancient Romans also liked cats. They thought cats were a
96	symbol of being free.
100	The mosaic (*moh-ZAY-ik*) above was made hundreds of years
108	ago in Italy. A mosaic is made from small colored squares of stone,
121	glass, or tiles. The squares are put together to make a picture. 133

Comprehension Check

1. What does the author want people to know about cats in ancient Egypt? **Author's Purpose**
2. How was the ancient Romans' belief about cats different from the ancient Egyptians'? **Compare and Contrast**

	Words Read	–	Number of Errors	=	Words Correct Score
First Read		–		=	
Second Read		–		=	

© Macmillan/McGraw-Hill

CA **R 1.6** Read aloud fluently and accurately and with appropriate intonation and expression.

Dictionaries and encyclopedias give different kinds of facts.

A. Write *dictionary* or *encyclopedia* to complete each description of a reference source.

1. A(n) _____ is a book or collection of books that gives detailed information about many different topics. Entries may include maps, charts, graphs, and photos.

2. A(n) _____ is a book that gives definitions of words, their pronunciations, parts of speech, and sometimes example sentences.

B. Which reference source would be better to help you find the following kinds of information?

3. What part of speech is the word *style*? _____

4. Where and when did the art of origami begin?

    _____

5. Who are some famous artists from Italy? _____

6. What does *piñata* mean? _____

© Macmillan/McGraw-Hill

CA R 2.0 Reading Comprehension

Compare/Contrast Writing Frame

Summarize *Music of the Stone Age.*
Use the Compare/Contrast Writing Frame below.

Both music today and music long ago are the **same** in some ways. They are the same because _____

_____

_____

_____.

However, in other ways music today and music long ago are **different**. They are different because _____

_____

_____

_____.

So, music today and music long ago have both **similarities and differences**.

Rewrite the completed summary on another sheet of paper. Keep it as a model for writing a summary of an article or selection using this text structure.

© Macmillan/McGraw-Hill

- Add **-ed** to most verbs to tell about an action in the past.
- If a verb ends with one consonant, double the consonant and add **-ed**.
- If a verb ends with **e**, drop the **e** and add **-ed**.

Find the mistakes in the letter. Rewrite it correctly below.

dear Emily

    Our teacher planed an awesome trip to the museum. We learnned all about dinosaurs. We watchd a movie about Tyrannosaurus Rex. We were most surprissed to see real dinosaur fossils.

            your friend

            Carlos

_____

_____

_____

_____

_____

CA **LC 1.3** Identify and correctly use various parts of speech, including nouns and verbs, in writing and speaking.

© Macmillan/McGraw-Hill

Name _____

A. There are six spelling mistakes in the paragraph below. Circle the misspelled words. Write the words correctly on the lines below.

My dog can run in the perk. During a storm, my dog hides under the couch. After dirk, my dog sleeps in bed with me. A horse is too big to sleep in a bed. It lives in a stable on a faerm. A horse likes to run fer. It eats a larg amount of food. I think dogs arre easier to take care of than horses.

I. _____   2. _____   3. _____

4. _____   5. _____   6. _____

B. Writing

Write about the needs of two different animals. Use four words from your spelling list.

_____

_____

_____

_____

© Macmillan/McGraw-Hill

LC 1.8 Spell basic short-vowel, long-vowel, *r*-controlled, and consonant-blend patterns correctly.

Music of the Stone Age
Grade 2/Unit 3   167

The letters *or*, *ore*, and *oar* stand for the same sound.

p**or**t   b**oar**   m**ore**

A. Write a word from the box to complete each question.

| chores | oar | shore | storm | soar | thorns |

1. Do those roses have _____?

2. What _____ do you do to help out at home?

3. Have you ever watched eagles _____ overhead?

4. Is it cooler by the _____ in the summer?

5. Does the rowboat have a spare _____?

6. How long do you think the _____ will last?

B. Use two words from the box in new sentences. Write the sentences on the lines.

7. _____

8. _____

© Macmillan/McGraw-Hill

CA   **R 1.1** Recognize and use knowledge of spelling patterns
(e.g., diphthongs, special vowel spellings) when reading.

**A. Choose a word from the box to finish each sentence.
Then write the word on the line.**

furious   neutral   emergency   impatient   demand   sincerely

1. Max felt _____ as he waited in line.

2. Ben knew Sally was mad at Jina, but he was

    _____ about it.

3. Milo was _____ thankful for the help.

4. The building caught fire, and everyone inside used the

    _____ exit.

5. Dad was _____ when he hit his thumb with
   the hammer.

6. We learned you cannot _____ more recess.

B. Write two sentences using a word from the box.

7. _____

   _____

8. _____

© Macmillan/McGraw-Hill

Name _____

- The past-tense form of **have** is **had**.
- Use **had** in the past tense with any subject.

I <u>had</u> a dance recital.

My friends <u>had</u> fun watching me dance.

Change the verb *have* from present tense to past tense in each sentence. Write the new sentence on the lines.

I. We have our dance show in January.

_____

2. The show has three parts.

_____

3. I have a lead role.

_____

4. Juanita has a solo.

_____

5. We have a party after the show.

_____

CA **LC 1.0** Written and Oral English Language Conventions

© Macmillan/McGraw-Hill

Name _____

A word part that is added to the end of a word to change its meaning is called a **suffix**.

     The suffix **-er** means "more than."

     The suffix **-est** means "most."

You can add the word endings **-er** and **-est** to make comparisons.

Add the suffixes -er or -est to the words in the box to complete each sentence.

hot	fast	long	small

The sun was shining. It was _____ than yesterday. My

friends and I ran two races in the park. The second race lasted

_____ than the first. I was the _____ in the

group. My little brother was at the park, too. He is _____

than me. When I got home, I took the _____ nap.

© Macmillan/McGraw-Hill

north	port	store	roar	board
oar	more	wore	tore	fort

A. Look at the spelling words in the box. Match each word with a spelling pattern.

or 1. _____ 2. _____

3. _____

ore 4. _____ 5. _____

6. _____ 7. _____

oar 8. _____ 9. _____

10. _____

B. X the Word

Look at the vowel spelling pattern in each row of spelling words. In each row, cross out the word that does not belong.

store	board	tore
oar	roar	port
fort	north	more
wore	board	roar
north	port	store

© Macmillan/McGraw-Hill

CA **LC 1.8** Spell basic short-vowel, long-vowel, *r*-controlled, and consonant-blend patterns correctly.

Name _____

**As you read *Click, Clack, Moo: Cows That Type*, fill in
the Cause and Effect Chart.**

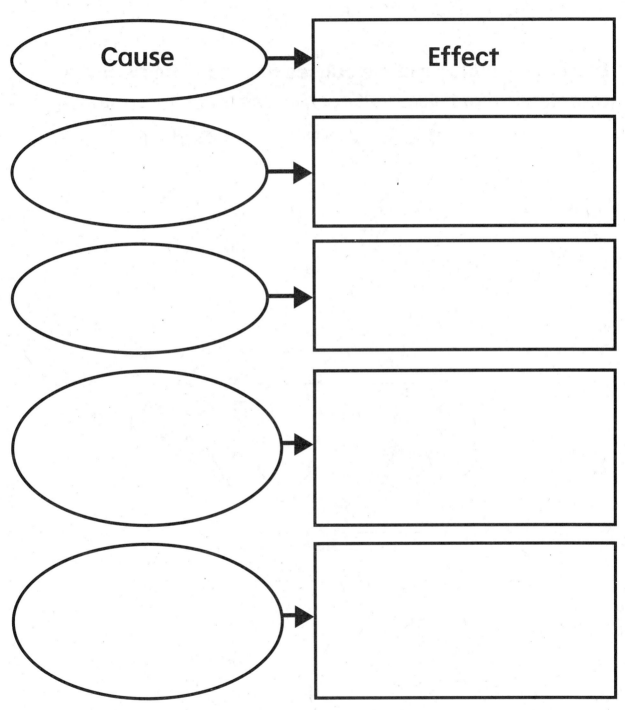

Cause	Effect

How does the information you wrote in this Cause and Effect Chart
help you to better understand *Click, Clack, Moo: Cows That Type*?

© Macmillan/McGraw-Hill

CA **R 2.6** Recognize cause-and-effect relationships in a text.

> The reason why or how something happens is the **cause**.
> An **effect** is what happens.

Look at the pictures of the causes and their effects. Write a sentence that tells about each cause and effect shown.

Cause	→	Effect

1.  →

_____

_____

2.  →

_____

_____

3.  →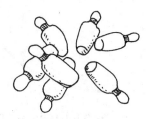

_____

CA **R 2.6** Recognize cause-and-effect relationships in a text.

© Macmillan/McGraw-Hill

Name _____

Synonyms are words that have almost the same meaning.
You can use a **thesaurus** to find synonyms for many words.

Cap and *lid* are synonyms.

I put the **cap** on the bottle.   I put the **lid** on the bottle.

**Replace *big* in each sentence with a synonym that
makes sense. Write the new sentence on the line.**

    big *adjective* **I.** Large in size: *The elephant is a **big** animal.*
large, gigantic, huge 2. Of great importance: *Our trip to Florida is
a **big** event for us.* **important, major, notable 3.** Grown-up: *When
I'm **big**, I'll be a doctor.* **adult, older, mature**

I. I am going to travel when I am big.

_____

2. It was a small wedding but a big event.

_____

3. Our yard is big so it takes a long time to mow it.

_____

4. We practiced hard for the big game.

_____

© Macmillan/McGraw-Hill

CA **R 1.7** Understand and explain common antonyms and **synonyms**.

Name _____

As I read, I will pay attention to pacing and intonation and expression when reading words that have special type.

	Next door was Farmer Rosie's farm. Farmer Rosie's sheep
9	were watching.
11	"What's going on next door?" they asked. "Selina, snoop
20	for us!"
22	Selina hid behind a fence post.
28	"They're knitting!" said Selina. "You hold two sticks and
37	some wool. Then you say a rhyme. *Knit and knit. Knit. Knitwit.*
49	*Make a sweater that will fit!"*
55	Now Farmer Rosie's sheep had Knitting Fever, too!
63	Then Selina had an idea. "Let's see who can knit the most
75	sweaters!" she shouted. "Our team will be the Woolly Sweaters."
85	"And our team will be the Knitwits," said Sharon.
94	"This is our rhyme," said Selina. *"You are good, but we are*
106	*better. You can't beat a Woolly Sweater!"* 113

Comprehension Check

1. Why do Farmer Rosie's sheep get Knitting Fever? **Cause and Effect**

2. What happens after Farmer Rosie's sheep get Knitting Fever? **Sequence**

	Words Read	–	Number of Errors	=	Words Correct Score
First Read		–		=	
Second Read		–		=	

© Macmillan/McGraw-Hill

(CA) **R 1.6** Read aloud fluently and accurately and with appropriate intonation and expression.

Name _____

Bar graphs use bars of different lengths to show the relationship between numbers.

Read the bar graph. Circle the correct answer to each question.

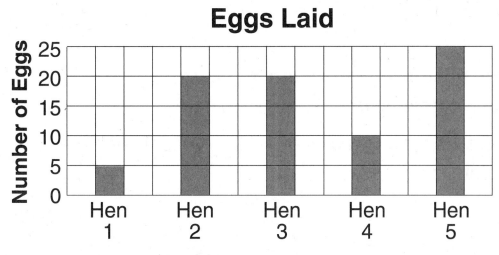

Eggs Laid

I. What is being compared?

    a. number of hens   **b.** number of eggs

2. Which hen laid the most eggs?

    a. Hen 2   **b.** Hen 3   **c.** Hen 4   **d.** Hen 5

3. Which laid the fewest eggs?

    a. Hen I   **b.** Hen 2   **c.** Hen 3   **d.** Hen 4

4. Which two hens laid the same number of eggs?

    a. Hen I and Hen 2   **b.** Hen 2 and Hen 3   **c.** Hen 3 and Hen 4

5. Which hen laid 10 eggs?

    a. Hen I   **b.** Hen 2   **c.** Hen 3   **d.** Hen 4

© Macmillan/McGraw-Hill

CA R 2.7 Interpret information from diagrams, charts, and graphs.

Click, Clack, Moo: Cows
That Type • **Grade 2/Unit 3** 177

Name _____

- Use **has** in the present tense when the subject is singular. Use **have** when the subject is plural or **I** or **you**.
- The past-tense form of **have** is **had**.
- Capitalize the first letter and each important word in a book title.

Circle the mistakes in the sentences. Write the sentences correctly on the lines.

I. Our class is making a play of the book charlie and the chocolate factory.

_____

_____

2. We have tryouts yesterday.

_____

3. Alison have a great singing voice.

_____

4. Three boys has the part of Charlie.

_____

5. You has to come see our show!

_____

CA   **LC 1.0** Written and Oral English Language Conventions

© Macmillan/McGraw-Hill

Name _____

A. There are six spelling mistakes in the paragraph below. Circle the misspelled words. Write the words correctly on the lines below.

Inventors have dreamed up many new things over the years. There are moar inventions today than ever before. Someone invented an oare to row a boat. Someone else invented a bord game called checkers. Long ago, if you woore your jeans and toare them, you would need to mend them by hand. Today you can fix them on a sewing machine. Or you can drive to a big department stoore and buy a new pair. What other inventions can you think of?

1. _____   2. _____

3. _____   4. _____

5. _____   6. _____

B. Writing

Write about your own idea for an invention. Use four words from the spelling list.

_____

_____

_____

LC 1.8 Spell basic short-vowel, long-vowel, r-controlled, and consonant-blend patterns correctly.

© Macmillan/McGraw-Hill

Click, Clack, Moo: Cows That Type • Grade 2/Unit 3

179

The letters *ar* stand for the ending sound you hear in *car*.

The letters *are* stand for the ending sound you hear in *bare*.

The letters *air* stand for the ending sound you hear in *chair*.

Write the words from the box that have the same vowel sound and spelling as the name of the picture.

star	stairs	flare	fair	pair	spare
glare	repair	care	cart	smart	afar

1. 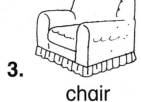   _____

car

2. 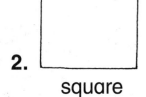   _____

square

3.    _____

chair

CA R 1.1 Recognize and use knowledge of spelling patterns
(e.g., diphthongs, special vowel spellings) when reading.

© Macmillan/McGraw-Hill

Name _____

A. Choose a word from the box to complete each sentence below. Then write the word on the line.

memories	imagination	familiar
glamorous	creating	occasions

1. People are _____ when they write books and draw pictures.

2. Birthdays and holidays are special _____ to celebrate.

3. _____ are made up of times people remember.

4. Something you know well is _____ to you.

5. You can use your _____ to make believe and think of a wild and crazy story.

6. A party that is fancy can also be _____ .

B. Use the words from the box to write two new sentences.

7. _____

   _____

8. _____

   _____

© Macmillan/McGraw-Hill

- If sentences have subjects that are the same, you can **combine** them.

- Sometimes you can combine sentences by joining two predicates with **and**.

    The cow slept.   The cow ate.

    The cow slept and ate.

Combine each pair of sentences by joining the predicates with the word *and*. Write the new sentences on the lines.

1. **a.** The cows walk in the field.
   b. The cows eat grass.

   _____

2. **a.** The farmer sits on a stool.
   b. The farmer milks the cow.

   _____

3. **a.** The pigs roll in the mud.
   b. The pigs get dirty.

   _____

4. **a.** The barn is big.
   b. The barn has red sides.

   _____

© Macmillan/McGraw-Hill

CA **LC 1.0** Written and Oral English Language Conventions

A **prefix** is a word part that can be added to the beginning of a word to change its meaning.

re- = "again"   **un-** = "not"   **dis-** = "opposite of"

Read each sentence. Write the meaning of the underlined word on the line below.

I. I wrote a story about my family, but I was <u>unhappy</u> with it.

_____

2. Mom <u>disagreed</u>. She thought the story was good.

_____

3. I decided to <u>rewrite</u> the story anyway.

_____

4. I wanted to <u>redo</u> the parts I did not like.

_____

5. Some parts seemed <u>unreal</u> and <u>dishonest</u>.

_____

6. I finished fixing my story. I <u>reread</u> it. Now, I like the story.

_____

© Macmillan/McGraw-Hill

Name _____

fair	care	star	hair	pair
shark	stare	dare	rare	chair

A. Word Sort

Look at the spelling words in the box. Match each word
with a spelling pattern.

ar   1. _____   2. _____

are   3. _____   4. _____

          5. _____   6. _____

air   7. _____   8. _____

          9. _____   10. _____

B. Misfit Letter

An extra letter has been added to each spelling word
below. Draw a line through the letter that does not
belong. Write the word correctly on the line.

11. caire _____   12. faire _____

13. paire _____   14. shairk _____

15. chaier _____

© Macmillan/McGraw-Hill

CA **LC 1.8** Spell basic short-vowel, long-vowel, *r*-controlled,
and consonant-blend patterns correctly.

Name _____

As you read *Stirring Up Memories*, fill in the Conclusion Chart.

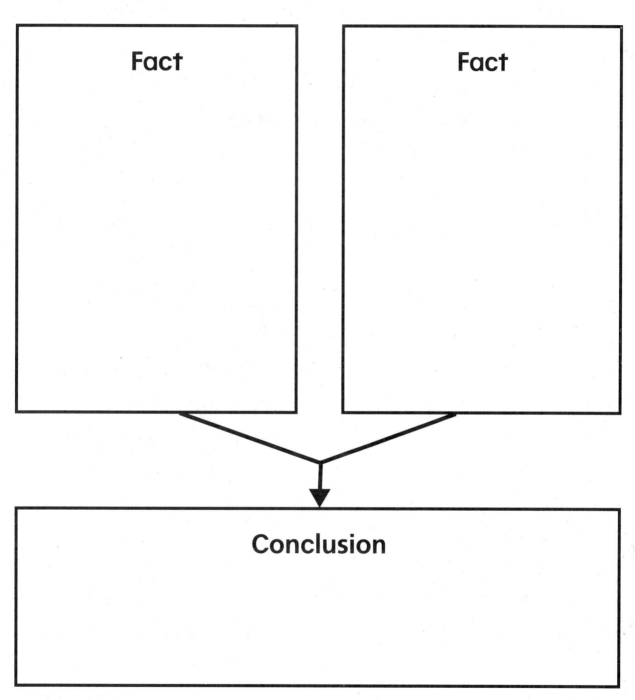

Fact	Fact

Conclusion

How does the information you wrote in the Conclusion Chart help you summarize *Stirring Up Memories*?

© Macmillan/McGraw-Hill

 R 2.0 Reading Comprehension

Name _____

When you **draw conclusions**, you make decisions about a story based on text and picture clues and what you already know.

Draw conclusions to answer each riddle. Use the words in the box.

| donkey | owl | raccoon | starfish |

1. I live in the water.

   I swim in the sea.

   Something in the sky

   Shares its name with me.

   What am I?

   _____

2. You might have heard me hoot.

   You might have seen me fly.

   Some say that I am wise.

   Can you guess? What am I?

   _____

3. I can't unlock a door.

   Still, my name has its own key.

   A horse and I look almost the same.

   Use this line to write my name.

   _____

4. I have rings around my eyes.

   I'm quite a sight to see.

   My tail has rings of black and white.

   Now, say, who could I be?

   _____

© Macmillan/McGraw-Hill

CA R 2.0 Reading Comprehension

Name _____

You can sometimes tell the meaning of unfamiliar words if you use what you know about **word parts** or **word roots**. Some words in English have Greek and Latin roots.

Read each root below. Circle that root in each word. Use both words in a sentence.

1. <u>Root:</u> **cycl**   The root *cycl* means *circle* or *ring*.

   bicycle   **cyclone**

   _____

   _____

2. <u>Root:</u> **act**   The root *act* means *do*.

   actor   **action**

   _____

   _____

3. <u>Root:</u> **graph**   The root *graph* means *write*.

   telegraph   **autograph**

   _____

   _____

© Macmillan/McGraw-Hill

As I read, I will pay attention to phrasing.

	People who can read are lucky. The world is full of words.
12	There are words in books and newspapers. There are
21	words on road signs and billboards. There are words on
31	maps and food labels. There are even words on television (TV)
42	and on your computer!
46	Words give us information. They can make us think. They
56	can make us laugh. They can make us cry.
65	Who puts these words together? Writers do. This book is
75	about different kinds of writers and how they use words.
85	Some writers write about the news. They write stories for
95	magazines, newspapers, the Internet, radio, and TV. They are
104	often "on the scene" for a news event. They **interview** people
115	there. Then they report the story as quickly as they can. 126

Comprehension Check

1. Do you think there are writers other than the ones who write the news? **Draw Conclusions**

2. Why do news writers have to report the news quickly? **Make Inferences**

	Words Read	−	Number of Errors	=	Words Correct Score
First Read		−		=	
Second Read		−		=	

© Macmillan/McGraw-Hill

CA **R 1.6** Read aloud fluently and accurately and with appropriate intonation and expression.

Name _____

Alliteration means starting several words in a row with the same letter. **Onomatopoeia** is the use of a word that sounds like the object or action it names.

The bees **buzz** from flower to flower.

The words below have onomatopoeia. Use each in a sentence and try to use alliteration in the sentences.

1. roar _____

_____

2. pop _____

_____

3. zip _____

_____

4. beep _____

_____

5. crunch _____

_____

6. splash _____

_____

© Macmillan/McGraw-Hill

- Sometimes you can **combine sentences** by joining two predicates with *and*.
- End a statement or a command with a period.
- End a question with a question mark.
- End an exclamation with an exclamation point.

Rewrite the paragraph correctly on the lines below. Add punctuation and combine sentences with the same subjects.

Have you ever been to a farm Our class went on a trip to a farm. Our class saw lots of animals. We watched baby chicks hop around We watched pigs play in the mud Boy, did those pigs get dirty

_____

_____

_____

_____

CA LC 1.0 Written and Oral English Language Conventions

© Macmillan/McGraw-Hill

A. There are six spelling mistakes in the paragraph below. Circle the misspelled words. Write the words correctly on the lines below.

Everyone in our class is writing a book. Mark's book is about a shairk. Jeff's book is about a shooting starr. My book is about how to take cair of your haire. After we write our books, we will illustrate them. Then we will sit in an author's chare and read our stories to each other. We might also have a book faire so the entire school can read our books.

1. _____ **2.** _____ **3.** _____

4. _____ **5.** _____ **6.** _____

B. Writing

Be an author! Write a story about something you know about or enjoy doing. Use four words from your spelling list.

_____

© Macmillan/McGraw-Hill

LC 1.8 Spell basic short-vowel, long-vowel, *r*-controlled, and consonant-blend patterns correctly.

Name _____

Two letter sounds blended together can make one vowel sound. Sometimes the letters **ow** or **ou** can stand for the same vowel sound. You can hear the sound of **ou** in **house** and the sound of **ow** in **cow**.

Read each word. Then circle the word next to it that has the same vowel sound.

1. south
   toy
   clown

2. ground
   wow
   tool

3. sound
   now
   one

4. shower
   show
   pound

5. power
   out
   point

6. clown
   round
   soil

7. cloud
   grow
   brown

8. loud
   loyal
   town

9. how
   mow
   ouch

10. howl
    mouth
    own

 R 1.1 Recognize and use knowledge of spelling patterns (e.g., **diphthongs**, special vowel spellings) when reading.

© Macmillan/McGraw-Hill

Name _____

Choose a word from the box to match each clue. Then write the answers in the puzzle.

| swung | gasped | delicious | frantically | attached |

Across

3. A baseball player _____ the bat to hit the ball.

4. Your head is _____ to your neck.

5. People who love pizza think it tastes _____.

Down

1. Kendra _____ searched for her lost dog.

2. The tired runner _____ when she won the race.

© Macmillan/McGraw-Hill

Name _____

- The past-tense form for **am** is **was**.
- The past-tense form for **is** is **was**.
- The past-tense form for **are** is **were**.

I <u>am</u> at the park. Yesterday, I <u>was</u> at the farm.

The chick <u>is</u> in the yard. Earlier, it <u>was</u> in the barn.

The bears <u>are</u> sleepy. In the spring, they <u>were</u> active.

Choose the correct linking verb in ( ). Then write the complete sentence below.

1. Yesterday I (was, were) in the woods.

   _____

2. There (was, were) a deer eating leaves.

   _____

3. The birds (was, were) in the air.

   _____

4. A squirrel (was, were) up in a tree.

   _____

5. It (was, were) very peaceful.

   _____

© Macmillan/McGraw-Hill

CA LC 1.0 Written and Oral English Language Conventions

Name _____

> Use **-s** or **-es** to make some words mean more than one.
> For words that end with a consonant and **y**, change the
> **y** to **i** and add **-es**.
>
> story − y + i + es = stories

Complete each sentence by changing the underlined word to mean more than one.

1. Max and his friend Ben wanted some <u>cherry</u>. _____

2. There are no cherry trees in <u>city</u>. _____

3. Cherry trees grow on <u>farm</u>. _____

4. Max and Ben went to a farm with their <u>father</u> _____
   and baby <u>sister</u> _____ .

5. The <u>boy</u> _____ needed help picking.

6. <u>Baby</u> _____ can't pick, so the sisters cannot help.

7. Max and Ben carried two large <u>basket</u> _____ .

8. Soon everyone was eating the red, ripe <u>berry</u>. _____

© Macmillan/McGraw-Hill

R 1.5 Identify and correctly use regular plurals (e.g., -s, -es, -ies) and
irregular plurals (e.g., *fly/flies, wife/wives*).

Head, Body, Legs
Grade 2/Unit 4
195

Name _____

| clown | ground | crown | shout | cloud |
| sound | house | brown | growl | howl |

A. Word Sort

Look at the spelling words in the box. Fill in the blanks below with spelling words that match each spelling pattern.

ow

1. _____
2. _____
3. _____
4. _____
5. _____

ou

6. _____
7. _____
8. _____
9. _____
10. _____

B. Rhyme Time

Write the spelling words that rhyme with each of these words.

11. pound

_____

_____

12. mouse

_____

13. owl

_____

_____

CA **LC 1.8** Spell basic short-vowel, long-vowel, *r*-controlled, and consonant-blend patterns correctly.

© Macmillan/McGraw-Hill

As you read *Head, Body, Legs: A Story from Liberia*, fill in the Cause and Effect Chart.

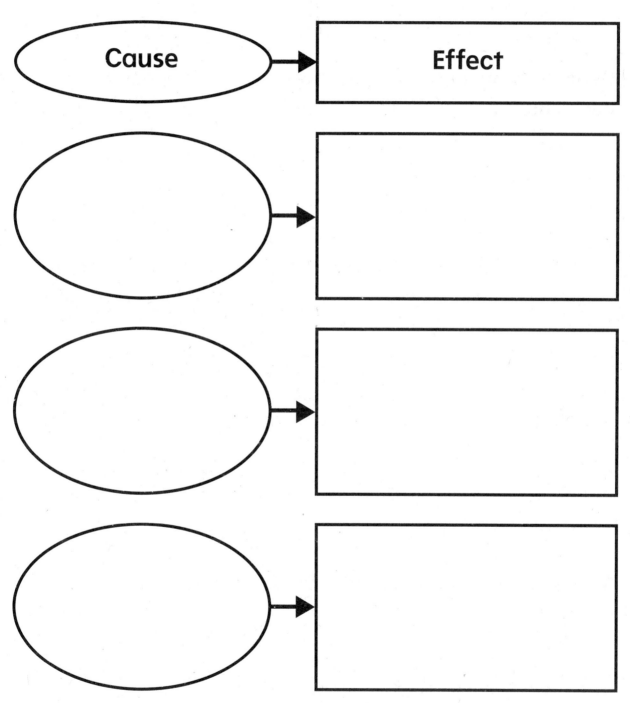

How does the information you wrote in this Cause and Effect Chart help you to better understand *Head, Body, Legs: A Story from Liberia*?

© Macmillan/McGraw-Hill

 R 2.6 Recognize cause-and-effect relationships in a text.

A **cause** is the reason something happens.

An **effect** is what happens.

Read the story about two brothers to find an effect for each cause below. Write the effect on the line.

    Bob wanted to put his new toy together, but he had a hard time doing it by himself. He asked his brother, Joe, to help him. First Joe got a screwdriver to help attach the wheels. Then Bob tried to put the doors on the car, but they wouldn't fit. Joe helped put the doors on. They turned on the car, but it did not move. Then Bob remembered that they needed to put batteries in the car. The car worked!

1. cause: Bob had a hard time putting his new toy together.

    effect: _____

2. cause: Bob and Joe wanted to attach the wheels to the car.

    effect: _____

3. cause: The car doors would not fit.

    effect: _____

4. cause: The toy car did not move.

    effect: _____

 R 2.6 Recognize cause-and-effect relationships in a text.

© Macmillan/McGraw-Hill

Sometimes the other words in a sentence can help you figure out the meaning of a new word. These words are **context clues** and can come before or after an unknown word.

Read each sentence. Then circle the meaning of the word in dark type.

1. The teacher let Lorna and me work on the project **together**, so each of us completed half of the work.

   with another person   alone

2. The **coach** helps us learn to throw and hit balls.

   person who trains a team   a type of ball

3. Each camper completed a **task** to help the camp.

   camp   job

4. Everyone got along and **cooperated** to get the job done.

   worked together   worked separately

5. Megan used a screwdriver to **assemble** the toy house.

   play with   build

6. All of us **participated** in the reading program by reading five books each.

   took part   ate

© Macmillan/McGraw-Hill

As I read, I will pay attention to the punctuation in each sentence.

	A fisherman lived with his wife in a little house.
10	Every morning he went to the sea. He tried to catch
21	fish to eat.
24	One day the fisherman caught nothing. Then he
32	felt a strong tug on his fishing line. The fishing rod
43	swung from side to side. The fisherman fought
51	**frantically** to hold on to it.
57	The fisherman reeled in the line. There
64	was a golden fish **attached** to his hook.
72	"Please let me go!" it cried. "I cannot breathe out
82	of water!"
84	The fish was beautiful. But it was too small to
94	eat, so the fisherman let it go. 101

Comprehension Check

1. What made the fisherman's fishing rod swing from side to side?
Draw Conclusions

2. Why did the fisherman go down to the sea every morning?
Cause and Effect

	Words Read	–	Number of Errors	=	Words Correct Score
First Read		–		=	
Second Read		–		=	

© Macmillan/McGraw-Hill

200 Head, Body, Legs
Grade 2/Unit 4

CA **R 1.6** Read aloud fluently and accurately and with appropriate intonation and expression.

Name _____

A home page on the Internet is the starting place for getting information. It has links to other related information on the Web site. A **drop-down menu** will help you find more links.

Look at the home page below. Then follow the directions and answer the question.

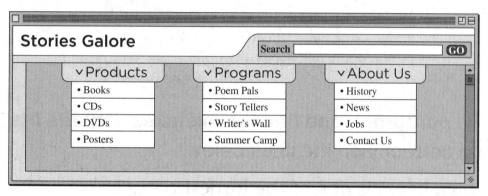

I. What is the title of this Web page?

_____

2. What are two links under Products?

_____

3. Where would you find the link Summer Camp?

_____

4. What would you click on to contact the president of Stories Galore?

_____

© Macmillan/McGraw-Hill

CA **R 2.7** Interpret information from diagrams, charts, and graphs.

Head, Body, Legs   **201**
Grade 2/Unit 4

- The words *is*, *are*, *am*, *was*, and *were* can be **linking verbs**.

Read the paragraph and find the mistakes. Rewrite the passage correctly on the lines below.

Brown bears is one of the largest types of bears. A female brown bear are about half the size of a male. These bears has thick fur that are usually brown. Some bears is lighter, and others is almost black. Brown bear cubs are born between january and march.

_____

_____

_____

_____

_____

© Macmillan/McGraw-Hill

CA **LC 1.0** Written and Oral English Language Conventions

A. There are six spelling mistakes in the report below. Circle the misspelled words. Write the words correctly on the lines below.

A desert is a hot, dry place. It may look broun because few green plants can survive there. Some animals can and do live in the desert. You may hear a lowd soond at night. What is it? It might be the houl of a coyote. Or it might be the groowl of a dingo. Dingoes are like dogs. Some dangerous animals live in the desert, too. If you see one of them, go back into your howse!

1. _____ 2. _____ 3. _____

4. _____ 5. _____ 6. _____

B. Writing

Write a short report about animals that live in the desert. Use four of the spelling words in your report.

_____

© Macmillan/McGraw-Hill

LC 1.8 Spell basic short-vowel, long-vowel, *r*-controlled, and consonant-blend patterns correctly.

Head, Body, Legs **203**
Grade 2/Unit 4

The letters *oi* and *oy* can stand for the vowel sound you hear in the words *joy* and *noise*.

Write the missing letters in each word. Then read the word.

1.

c ___ ___ n s

2.

b ___ ___

3.

p ___ ___ n t

4.

b ___ ___ l

5.

t ___ ___ s

6.

___ ___ l

CA **R 1.1** Recognize and use knowledge of spelling patterns (e.g., diphthongs, special vowel spellings) when reading.

© Macmillan/McGraw-Hill

Name _____

A. Read the passage. Choose a word from the box to complete each sentence. Write it on the line.

| tips | obeys | accident | buddy | enormous | attention |

Our class took a field trip to the zoo. I couldn't believe how big

the zoo was. It was _____! Each of us had to hold

hands with a _____. We paid _____
to our teacher. He told us the rules. He said, "A good student

_____ the rules. Following rules can keep you

from having an _____. I don't want you to get
hurt or lost." Our teacher also gave us good ideas about what to

look for at the zoo. His _____ helped us have a
good time.

B. Use two vocabulary words to write two new sentences.

1. _____

2. _____

© Macmillan/McGraw-Hill

Name _____

- A **helping verb** helps another verb show an action.
- *Is, are, am, was,* and ***were*** can be helping verbs.

    A fox <u>is</u> looking for food.
    The bears <u>are</u> hibernating.
    I <u>am</u> watching the birds fly south.
    The squirrels <u>were</u> gathering nuts.

**Choose the correct helping verb in ( ).
Then write the complete sentence
below.**

I. The chicks (was, were) following their mother.

_____

2. The mother bird (was, were) protecting her babies.

_____

3. One chick (is, are) pecking around for food.

_____

4. Another chick (is, are) hiding behind its mother.

_____

5. I (am, are) watching the chicks.

_____

© Macmillan/McGraw-Hill

CA **LC 1.3** Identify and correctly use various parts of speech, including nouns and **verbs**, in writing and speaking.

Name _____

A **prefix** is a word part that can be added to the beginning of a word to change the word's meaning.

re- = "again"   *un-* = "not"   *dis-* = "opposite of"

Read each sentence. Then write the meaning of the underlined word on the line below.

1. Jed fills in the hole and redigs it.

   _____

2. The team of workers will fix the unsafe road.

   _____

3. The team disagreed about the best way to do the job.

   _____

4. Jack's friends wanted him to rejoin the baseball team.

   _____

5. Sara must review the notes she wrote.

   _____

6. The team was unsure what to do next.

   _____

© Macmillan/McGraw-Hill

Name _____

boil	moist	joy	toy	point
broil	soil	avoid	royal	oil

A. Word Sort

Look at the spelling words in the box. Write the spelling
words that have the *oi* pattern.

1. _____ 2. _____ 3. _____

4. _____ 5. _____ 6. _____

7. _____

Write the spelling words that have the *oy* pattern.

8. _____ 9. _____ 10. _____

B. Missing Letter

A letter is missing from each spelling word below. Write
the missing letter in the box. Then write the spelling word
correctly on the line.

11. brol ☐ _____

12. roal ☐ _____

13. moit ☐ _____

14. pont ☐ _____

15. sil ☐ _____

© Macmillan/McGraw-Hill

CA **LC 1.8** Spell basic short-vowel, long-vowel, *r*-controlled, and
consonant-blend patterns correctly.

As you read *Officer Buckle and Gloria*, fill in the Illustrations Chart.

Illustration	What I Learn from the Picture

How does the information you wrote in this Illustrations Chart help you to better understand *Officer Buckle and Gloria*?

Name _____

Illustrations are pictures that go with a story or article. They can help you understand what you are reading.

Look at each illustration and read the sentence. Use the illustration to help you answer the question. Then fill in the circle in front of the correct answer.

1. The girl wore her safety gear when she skated. Which is part of <u>safety gear</u>?
   ⓐ window
   ⓑ helmet
   ⓒ dog

2. The boy put on his life jacket so he could go on the boat. Which letter shows the <u>life jacket</u>?
   ⓐ a
   ⓑ b
   ⓒ c

3. We stayed on the curb because the bus was approaching. An approaching school bus is _____.
   ⓐ leaving
   ⓑ coming
   ⓒ stopped

4. We were careful to keep our hands away from the porcupine. What is a <u>porcupine</u>?
   ⓐ a drink
   ⓑ a hat
   ⓒ an animal

© Macmillan/McGraw-Hill

CA R 2.0 Reading Comprehension

Name _____

Synonyms are words that have the same or almost the same meaning.

Read each pair of sentences. A word in the first sentence and a word in the second sentence are synonyms. Circle the synonyms. Then write them on the lines.

I. It was time for Gina to go.

She was ready to leave.

_____ _____

2. Gina put on her helmet to begin her bike ride.

She could not wait to start.

_____ _____

3. Gina had to ride her mom's big bike.

The large bike was a little bit hard to ride.

_____ _____

4. Gina was careful as she rode quickly.

She wanted to get to her friend's house fast.

_____ _____

© Macmillan/McGraw-Hill

CA R 1.7 Understand and explain common antonyms and **synonyms**.

Officer Buckle and Gloria
Grade 2/Unit 4

211

As I read, I will pay attention to the phrasing in each sentence and my intonation.

	Roads can be dangerous places. Pay attention when you
9	are on or near a road. If you are not careful, an accident
22	may happen. Here are some tips to keep you safe.
32	Always walk on the sidewalk. If there is no sidewalk,
42	walk on the side of the road. Face cars coming toward you.
54	You should also be careful when crossing the road.
63	A safe pedestrian obeys these rules.
69	Follow these five steps when you need to cross the road:
80	**Step 1: STOP** at the side of the road.
88	**Step 2: LOOK** for any traffic.
93	**Step 3: LISTEN** for any traffic that might be coming.
102	**Step 4: WAIT** until there is no traffic before you cross.
112	**Step 5: GO** when it is safe to cross. 120

Comprehension Check

1. Why should you pay attention when you are on or near a road?
   Main Idea and Details

2. Why do you think it is a good idea to wait until there is no traffic to cross the street? **Make Inferences**

	Words Read	−	Number of Errors	=	Words Correct Score
First Read		−		=	
Second Read		−		=	

© Macmillan/McGraw-Hill

CA **R 1.6** Read aloud fluently and accurately and with appropriate intonation and expression.

Name _____

A **floor plan** is a small map of a building. It shows where you can find rooms and other things in a building.

Read the floor plan. Then circle the correct answer to complete each sentence.

I. Tam is in the lunchroom. The nearest exit for Tam is _____.

   a. exit A   **b.** exit B

2. Joe is in Room 3. The nearest exit for Joe is _____.

   a. exit B   **b.** exit A

3. The lunchroom is right across the hall from _____.

   a. the gym and Room I   **b.** the office and Room 2

4. The gym is right across the hall from _____.

   a. Room 3   **b.** the lunchroom

5. The second room on the left is _____.

   a. the gym   **b.** the lunchroom

6. Moe is in Room I. The nearest exit for Moe is _____.

   a. the front door   **b.** exit B

© Macmillan/McGraw-Hill

CA R 2.7 Interpret information from diagrams, charts, and graphs.

Officer Buckle and Gloria
Grade 2/Unit 4
213

- *Have, has, is, are, am, was,* and *were* can be **helping verbs**.
- Use quotation marks at the beginning and end of what a person says.

Read the paragraph and find the mistakes. Rewrite the passage correctly on the lines below.

In school we is learning about gorillas. Gorillas are large and gentle apes said our teacher. We read that they live in africa. We has also learned that gorillas eat vegetables. I is excited to learn more about gorillas.

_____

_____

_____

_____

_____

_____

_____

© Macmillan/McGraw-Hill

(CA) **LC 1.3** Identify and correctly use various parts of speech, including nouns and **verbs**, in writing and speaking.

Name _____

A. There are six spelling mistakes in the paragraph below. Circle the misspelled words. Write the words correctly on the lines below.

Once I was in a play about a king and queen. The stage was a rouyal castle. The queen wanted to avoyid cooking. She had her servant boel water for her tea. The king was very funny. He put soy sauce on everything he ate! I played the king and queen's child. I brought them great joiy. My favorite toiy in the castle was a nutcracker. The nutcracker squeaked when I used it. I learned how to oel it so it did not make any noise. The play was fun!

I. _____   2. _____   3. _____

4. _____   5. _____   6. _____

B. Writing

Write about acting in a play. Use four or five of your spelling words. Circle the spelling words you use.

_____

_____

_____

_____

CA **LC 1.8** Spell basic short-vowel, long-vowel, *r*-controlled, and consonant-blend patterns correctly.

Name _____

The letters **oo**, **ui**, and **ew** can make the same vowel sound.

new suit

broom

screw

Write a word from the box to fit each clue.

kangaroo	suit	stew	hoot	fruit
juice	grew	goose	flew	chew

1. This is the sound an owl makes. _____

2. This is something hot to eat. _____

3. A bird did this to get to the top of a tree. _____

4. Apples and grapes belong to this food group. _____

5. This is something you wear. _____

6. This animal hops, but it is not a rabbit. _____

7. You do this with your teeth. _____

8. This is something you can drink. _____

CA **R 1.1** Recognize and use knowledge of spelling patterns (e.g., diphthongs, special vowel spellings) when reading.

© Macmillan/McGraw-Hill

Name _____

A. Choose a word from the box to complete the letter.

serious	aid	personal	informs	heal

Dear María,

I have big news! I fell next to the pool at camp and now I have a broken arm. The fall was very _____, but the camp leaders came to my _____. The doctors told me I will _____ quickly. My family came for a visit as soon as they found out. They got here in just a few hours.

When a kid is hurt, the hospital always

_____ parents right away. The camp let me have a _____ day so I could visit with my family. I am staying at camp until it is over, but no more swimming for me! Let me know how you are.

Your friend always,
Ricky

B. Choose one word from the box to write a P.S. to the letter.

P.S.: _____

_____

© Macmillan/McGraw-Hill

Name _____

- The verbs **say** and **see** have special forms in the past tense.

I, we, you, they	<u>see</u>	saw
I, we, you, they	<u>say</u>	said

Rewrite the sentences using the past tense of the verb in dark type.

1. I **see** a boy litter.

_____

2. I **say,** "Don't pollute!"

_____

3. We **see** him pick up his garbage.

_____

4. "Thank you!" we **say**.

_____

5. The children **see** lots of people litter.

_____

6. "Clean up!" the children **say** to all of them.

_____

© Macmillan/McGraw-Hill

CA **LC 1.0** Written and Oral English Language Conventions

Name _____

A word part that is added to the end of a word to change its meaning is called a **suffix**.

     The suffix **-less** means "**without**."

     The suffix **-ful** means "**full of**."

When you add **-ful** or **-less** to a word that ends with **y**, you drop the **y** and add **i** before adding the suffix.

     mercy + ful = merciful

Write a word that means the same as the group of words. Your new word will end in -less or -ful.

1. full of beauty

_____

2. full of health

_____

3. without pain

_____

4. full of cheer

_____

5. without a clue

_____

6. full of taste

_____

7. without harm

_____

8. full of fancy

_____

© Macmillan/McGraw-Hill

Name _____

suit	shoe	room	clue	fruit
glue	flew	canoe	new	tool

A. Word Sort

Look at the spelling words in the box. Write the spelling words that match each spelling pattern.

oo

1. _____
2. _____

ue

3. _____
4. _____

ui

5. _____
6. _____

ew

7. _____
8. _____

oe

9. _____
10. _____

B. Rhyme Around

Write the spelling word that completes each rhyme.

11. Dad has a funny suit. The pattern on it is made of _____.

12. The toy plane flew because it was brand _____.

13. We were riding in the canoe when I lost my right _____.

14. I will give you a clue. This sticky stuff smells like _____.

15. I will get a pan and broom to clean up my messy _____.

© Macmillan/McGraw-Hill

CA **LC 1.8** Spell basic short-vowel, long-vowel, r-controlled, and consonant-blend patterns correctly.

Name _____

As you read _A Trip to the Emergency Room_, fill in the Sequence Chart.

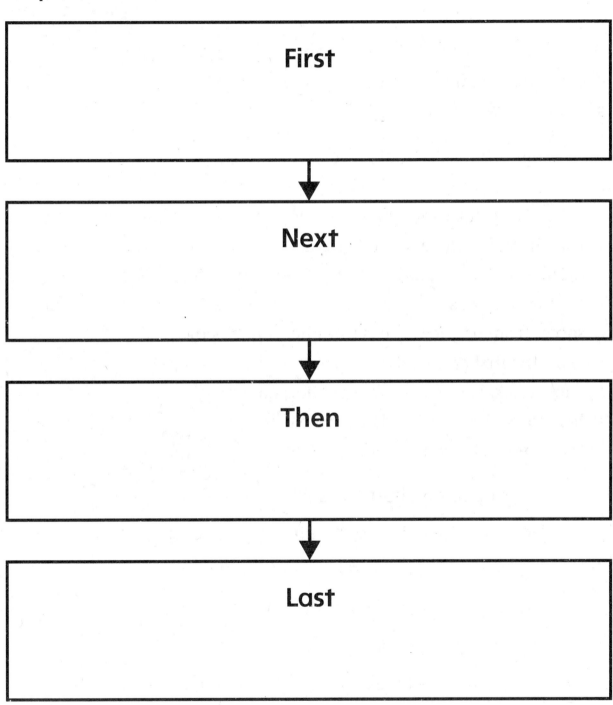

First

Next

Then

Last

How does the information you wrote in this Sequence Chart help you summarize _A Trip to the Emergency Room_?

© Macmillan/McGraw-Hill

Name _____

Sequence is the order in which events in a story happen.

**Read the story and the sentences below it. Number
the sentences from 1 to 6 to show the order of the
story events.**

A big storm left puddles everywhere. After school at soccer
practice, Liza slipped in the mud. She hurt her ankle and couldn't
get up. Coach Grimes put an ice pack on Liza's ankle. Liza's dad
was there. He drove her to the emergency room. "I hope you
didn't break your ankle, honey," Liza's dad said. The doctor said
Liza's ankle was sprained, not broken. He told Liza to stay off the
soccer field for a few weeks until her ankle healed.

In the first game Liza played after she
came back, Liza scored the winning goal for
her team. "I feel as good as new. No, better
than new!" she told her dad.

_____ Liza slipped and hurt her ankle.

_____ Liza's dad drove her to the emergency room.

_____ Liza told her dad she felt better than new.

_____ Liza came back and scored the winning goal.

_____ There was a big storm.

_____ The doctor said Liza's ankle was sprained.

© Macmillan/McGraw-Hill

Homophones are words that sound the same but have different meanings and different spellings. When you come to a new word that sounds the same as another word you know, you can use a dictionary to look up the word's meaning.

Study the dictionary entries. Then write a new sentence for each homophone.

knows *verb* is aware of or understands something. *Alex knows that summer begins in June.*

nose *noun* the part of the face we breathe and smell with. *The boy covered his nose before he sneezed.*

1. _____

2. _____

weak *adjective* not strong. *Grandma was weak during her illness.*

week *noun* a period of seven days in a row. *We went on vacation for a week.*

3. _____

4. _____

© Macmillan/McGraw-Hill

As I read, I will pay attention to the pronunciation of vocabulary words.

	Your body is working even when you are just
9	sitting still. You can see, hear, smell, taste, and feel.
19	Your body knows when it is cold or hot. It can
30	even **heal** itself when a part is broken or you feel
41	sick.
42	Sometimes a doctor can help your body get well.
51	A doctor can also give you a **personal** checkup
60	once a year to be sure you stay healthy.
69	Let's take a look at the human body. Then
78	we will see how a doctor can help you keep it
89	healthy. 90

Comprehension Check

1. When should you get a personal checkup? **Sequence**

2. How do you know that your body is working even when you are still? **Make and Confirm Predictions**

	Words Read	–	Number of Errors	=	Words Correct Score
First Read		–		=	
Second Read		–		=	

© Macmillan/McGraw-Hill

(CA) **R 1.6** Read aloud fluently and accurately and with appropriate intonation and **expression**.

Name _____

You can use the **Internet** to do research. A **search engine** is a program on the Internet that helps you find information on the World Wide Web. A **URL** is the address of a Web site. A **home page** is the main page of a Web site.

Carl used the Internet to research broken arms. Use his search results to answer the questions below.

Search Engine **Kidlookup**

How do I know if my arm is broken? Learn about what to look to know if an injured arm might be broken. http://www.firstaid.com/broken_arm	Treatments for broken arms: Types of casts Learn about the different kinds of casts doctors use to treat broken arms. http://www.healthcare.com/casts	Bike Safety: How to prevent injuries This site tells about important bike safety tips to protect riders from common injuries. http://ridesafely.com

1. What is the name of the search engine Carl used?

   _____

2. What is the URL of the site that tells about types of casts?

   _____

3. Which Web site would be best to use if you hurt your arm and wanted to find out if it might be broken?

   _____

4. Which Web site would not help Carl learn about broken arms and how to treat them?

   _____

© Macmillan/McGraw-Hill

Sequence Writing Frame

Summarize *A Trip to the Emergency Room*.
Use the Sequence Writing Frame below.

When you are sick or injure yourself, you sometimes have to go to the emergency room.

The **first** person you see is _____. That person _____

_____

_____.

Next, you see _____. That person _____

_____

_____.

Finally, you see _____. That person _____

_____

_____.

All these people work together to help the sick and injured.

Rewrite the completed summary on another sheet of paper. Keep it as a model for writing a summary of an article or selection using this text structure.

© Macmillan/McGraw-Hill

CA R 2.0 Reading Comprehension

Name _____

- The verbs *come*, *run*, *give*, and *sing* have special forms in the past tense.
- Begin the first word and each important word in a book title with a capital letter.
- Underline all the words in the title of a book.

Read the paragraph and find the mistakes. Rewrite the passage correctly on the lines below.

Only two friends comed to my party because of the blizzard. We runned around in the snow and had fun. One friend give me a book called blizzards and ice storms. What a perfect present, I said. Then they singed Happy Birthday to me, and we ate cake.

_____

_____

_____

_____

_____

© Macmillan/McGraw-Hill

Name _____

A. There are five spelling mistakes in the paragraph below. Circle the misspelled words. Write the words correctly on the lines below.

Dave was in his rewm when he saw the weather report. A nue cold front was on its way. There was going to be a big winter storm. The big gray clouds were one clew that snow would start falling soon. Dave rushed to the airport. Somehow the pilot floo the plane and landed it before the storm began. Dave saw his friend get off the plane in a sute. Dave gave him a heavy winter coat and gloves for his cold visit to Chicago.

1. _____   2. _____   3. _____

4. _____   5. _____

B. Writing

Write about a big storm.
Use five words from your spelling list.

_____

_____

_____

_____

_____

CA LC 1.8 Spell basic short-vowel, long-vowel, r-controlled, and consonant-blend patterns correctly.

© Macmillan/McGraw-Hill

Name _____

The letters *oo* and *ou* can stand for the vowel sound you hear in *cook* and *should*.

A. Read each word. Write a new word that rhymes. Then underline the letters in each word that make the sound you hear in the middle of *cook* and *should*.

1. stood   _____

2. shook   _____

3. soot   _____

4. could   _____

5. brook   _____

6. good   _____

B. Write two sentences using two of the words you wrote above.

7. _____

8. _____

© Macmillan/McGraw-Hill

R 1.1 Recognize and use knowledge of spelling patterns (e.g., diphthongs, special vowel spellings) when reading.

Choose a word from the box to answer each question. Write the word on the line.

> young   normal   rescued   examines   mammal   hunger

I. What is another word for *saved*? _____

2. Which word names a kind of animal that drinks its mother's milk and has

hair or fur? _____

3. Which word best tells about someone

who is not old? _____

4. Which word tells what a doctor does to an animal to see if

it is well? _____

5. Which word tells about the feeling an animal has when it needs

to eat? _____

6. Which word tells about something that is not odd?

_____

© Macmillan/McGraw-Hill

CA R 1.0 Word Analysis, Fluency, and Systematic Vocabulary Development

- Some verbs do not add **-ed** to form the past tense.
- The verbs **give** and **sing** have special forms in the past tense.

  I, we, you, they   give   gave
  I, we, you, they   sing   sang

Change the words in dark type to past tense. Write the new sentences on the lines below.

1. I **sing** the song about raindrops.

   _____

2. I **give** my old snow boots to my little brother.

   _____

3. We **sing** in a high voice.

   _____

4. They **sing** in a low voice.

   _____

5. We **give** our winter coats to charity.

   _____

6. You **give** money for hurricane victims, too.

   _____

© Macmillan/McGraw-Hill

LC 1.3 Identify and correctly use various parts of speech, including nouns and **verbs**, in writing and speaking.

A Harbor Seal Pup Grows Up   **231**
Grade 2/Unit 4

The letters *-ing* can be added to the end of a verb to change its tense.

If a word ends in silent *e*, drop the *e* before adding *-ing*.

smile – e + ing = smiling

**Add *-ing* to the end of each word. Write the new word.
Then use the word in a sentence.**

1. dive _____

_____

2. make _____

_____

3. snore _____

_____

4. ride _____

_____

© Macmillan/McGraw-Hill

CA **R 1.0** Word Analysis, Fluency, and Systematic Vocabulary Development

Name _____

| would | shook | should | hook | could |
| soot | brook | foot | crook | good |

A. Word Sort

Look at the spelling words in the box. Match the spelling word with the spelling pattern and write the word.

oot   1. _____   2. _____

ook   3. _____   4. _____

5. _____   6. _____

ood   7. _____

ould 8. _____   9. _____

10. _____

B. Pattern Smart

Write the spelling words that have the same pattern as *book*.

11. _____   12. _____

13. _____   14. _____

Write the spelling word that has the same pattern as *hood*.

15. _____

© Macmillan/McGraw-Hill

LC 1.8 Spell basic short-vowel, **long-vowel**, *r*-controlled, and consonant-blend patterns correctly.

As you read *A Harbor Seal Pup Grows Up*, **fill in the Sequence Chart.**

First

↓

Next

↓

Last

How does the information you wrote in this Sequence Chart help you better understand *A Harbor Seal Pup Grows Up*?

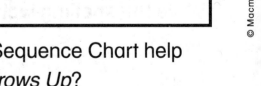
CA **R 2.0** Reading Comprehension

© Macmillan/McGraw-Hill

Name _____

The **sequence of events** is the order in which things happen. Words such as *first*, *then*, *next*, and *last* give clues to when events take place.

Read the story. Then write sentences that tell what happened first, next, then, and last on the lines below.

First, a kitten raced up a tree after a bird. Before she knew it, the kitten was stuck. She was high on a branch and couldn't get down. Next, the kitten cried and cried. Then a boy came along. He scooped up the kitten and placed her gently on the grass. At last the kitten was safe.

1. First _____

2. Next _____

3. Then _____

4. Last _____

_____

© Macmillan/McGraw-Hill

> **Antonyms** are words that have opposite or almost opposite meanings.

Circle the antonyms in each pair of sentences. Then write them on the lines.

1. I remember my first animal rescue. _____

   I knew it would not be my last. _____

2. My neighbor lost her puppy. _____

   I found him the next day. _____

3. The puppy did not go very far. _____

   He was near the park behind my house. _____

4. The puppy was shaking from the cold. _____

   His fur could not keep him warm in all the snow. _____

5. I bent down to see if the puppy was alright. _____

   He let me pick him up to carry him home. _____

© Macmillan/McGraw-Hill

CA R 1.7 Understand and explain common **antonyms** and synonyms.

Name _____

As I read, I will pay attention to phrasing.

	All tigers have stripes. But each tiger has different
9	stripes.
10	Tigers live in jungles and forests. A tiger's coat
19	helps it blend in with long grass, bushes, and trees.
29	This helps keep the tiger safe.
35	Tigers are mammals. A **mammal** feeds its
42	**young** on milk. Tiger cubs live with their mother for
52	two to three years. Adult male tigers live alone.
61	Tigers hunt alone. They hide and then sneak up
70	on their prey. They catch deer, wild pigs, and cattle. 80

Comprehension Check

1. How does a tiger's diet change as it grows up? **Sequence**

2. How do stripes help a tiger? **Main Idea and Details**

	Words Read	–	Number of Errors	=	Words Correct Score
First Read		–		=	
Second Read		–		=	

© Macmillan/McGraw-Hill

CA **R 1.6** Read aloud fluently and accurately and with appropriate
intonation and expression.

A **simile** compares one thing to another. Similes use the
words *like* or *as*.

**Read each question. Answer it with a complete sentence that
includes the underlined simile from the question. Then draw a
picture to show what is happening in the sentence.**

1. When might a person be <u>as hungry as a bear</u>?

_____

_____

_____
| |
| |
| |
| |
| |
| |
| |
|_____|

2. What might people be doing when they are <u>as busy as bees</u>?

_____

_____

_____
| |
| |
| |
| |
| |
| |
| |
|_____|

© Macmillan/McGraw-Hill

- The verbs **come**, **run**, **give**, and **sing** have special forms in the past tense.
- The first word and each important word in a book title begin with a capital letter.
- Underline all the words in the title of a book.

Read the paragraph and find the mistakes. Rewrite the passage correctly on the lines below.

Only two friends comed to my party because of the blizzard. We runned around in the snow and had fun. One friend give me a book called blizzards and ice storms. What a perfect present, I said. Then they singed Happy Birthday to me, and we ate cake.

_____

_____

_____

_____

_____

© Macmillan/McGraw-Hill

CA **LC 1.3** Identify and correctly use various parts of speech, including nouns and **verbs**, in writing and speaking.

A Harbor Seal Pup Grows Up
Grade 2/Unit 4

239

A. There are six spelling mistakes in the paragraph below. Circle the misspelled words. Write the words correctly on the lines below.

Our class stood by the brouk. It was littered with trash. We knew we shood do something. We got some garbage bags and gloves. We started picking up the trash. Jan's fut almost slipped into the brook. We had to be careful. Someone cuold get hurt. But we knew everyone woold be very happy that we took gud care of the brook.

1. _____   2. _____   3. _____

4. _____   5. _____   6. _____

B. Writing

Write about cleaning up something to make Earth a better place. Use four spelling words from your list.

_____

_____

_____

_____

© Macmillan/McGraw-Hill

CA **LC 1.8** Spell basic short-vowel, **long-vowel**, *r*-controlled, and consonant-blend patterns correctly.

Name _____

The letters *au* and *aw* often stand for the same sounds. You can hear these sounds **c*au*ght** and **cl*aw***.

Choose the word from the box that best matches each picture and clue. Then write it on the line below.

sauce	yawn	laundry	straw	sausage

I. This is clothing that needs to be washed.

_____

2. This is something that can help you drink.

_____

3. This can be good with spaghetti. _____

4. You may do this when you are tired.

_____

5. You might eat this for breakfast. _____

© Macmillan/McGraw-Hill

A. Choose the correct word from the box to match each definition below. Write the word on the line. Then number the words so they are in ABC order.

| fetch | simmered | menu | assembled | devoured |

1. put together _____ ____

2. to go get _____ ____

3. cooked on low heat on a stove _____ ____

4. ate greedily _____ ____

5. foods being served _____ ____

B. Write two sentences using words from the box.

6. _____

_____

7. _____

_____

© Macmillan/McGraw-Hill

Name _____

- A **contraction** is a short form of two words.
- An **apostrophe** (') takes the place of the letters that are left out.
- ***Doesn't***, ***don't***, ***didn't***, and ***can't*** are contractions.

  does not = <u>doesn't</u>   do not = <u>don't</u>

  did not = <u>didn't</u>   can not = <u>can't</u>

Replace the underlined words with contractions. Write the new sentences on the lines.

1. Many animals <u>can not</u> live in the Arctic.

_____

2. They <u>do not</u> do well in the cold weather.

_____

3. Most birds <u>can not</u> live in the Arctic all year.

_____

4. The tern <u>does not</u> stay for the winter.

_____

5. <u>Do not</u> be afraid of the Arctic wolf.

_____

6. The Arctic hare <u>did not</u> see the wolf.

_____

© Macmillan/McGraw-Hill

Name _____

The letters **-ed** can be added to the end of a verb to change its tense.

If a word ends in silent **e**, drop the **e** before adding **-ed**.

like – e + ed = liked

Add -ed to the end of each word. Write the new word.
Then use the word in a sentence.

1. paste _____

_____

2. name _____

_____

3. like _____

_____

4. close _____

_____

© Macmillan/McGraw-Hill

CA R 1.0 Word Analysis, Fluency, and Systematic Vocabulary Development

Name _____

| launch | draw | hawk | sauce | pause |
| law | crawl | fault | raw | jaw |

A. Word Sort

Look at the spelling words in the box. Write the spelling
words that have the *au* pattern.

1. _____ 2. _____ 3. _____

4. _____

Write the spelling words that have the *aw* pattern.

5. _____ 6. _____ 7. _____

8. _____ 9. _____ 10. _____

B. Missing Letter

A letter is missing from each spelling word below. Write
the missing letter in the box. Then write the spelling
word correctly on the line.

11. pase ☐ _____

12. hak ☐ _____

13. lanch ☐ _____

14. cral ☐ _____

15. falt ☐ _____

© Macmillan/McGraw-Hill

LC 1.8 Spell basic short-vowel, long-vowel, *r*-controlled, and
consonant-blend patterns correctly.

**As you read *Mice and Beans*, fill in the
Fantasy and Reality Chart.**

REALITY	FANTASY
What Could Happen?	What Could Not Happen?

How does the information you wrote in this Fantasy and Reality
Chart help you to better understand *Mice and Beans*?

R 2.0 Reading Comprehension

© Macmillan/McGraw-Hill

Name _____

Fantasy is something that cannot happen in real life.

Reality is something that can happen in real life.

Read each sentence. Write *reality* if it tells
about something that could really happen.
Write *fantasy* if it tells about something that
could not really happen.

1. The chair walked across the street. _____

2. The birds flew across the sky. _____

3. Keith ate five hot dogs. _____

4. Lauren is starting school tomorrow. _____

5. The goat was shopping at the mall. _____

6. The fairy granted Megan three wishes. _____

7. The cat meowed. _____

8. The dragon flew over the castle. _____

9. Rainbows have many colors. _____

10. The giant lifted the house with one hand. _____

© Macmillan/McGraw-Hill

You can figure out the meaning of an inflected **verb** by putting together the meanings of its **word parts**.

Add the word ending to the verb.
Then write the new word in a sentence.

1. wear + ing _____

_____

2. celebrate + ed _____

_____

3. laugh + s _____

_____

4. confirm + ing _____

_____

5. giggle + s _____

_____

6. heal + ed _____

_____

© Macmillan/McGraw-Hill

CA R 1.0 Word Analysis, Fluency, and Systematic Vocabulary Development

Name _____

As I read, I will pay attention to my expression.

	Roger woke up with the hot sun already smiling
9	down on him. He felt like it was going to be a
21	special day, but he wasn't sure why.
28	"It's the first day of summer!" said Dad.
36	That was it! Summer was here! It was Roger's
45	favorite time of the year. He thought about the
54	warm sun and the sweet fruits he ate each summer.
64	This year would be no different.
70	Roger and his dad always threw a party to
79	celebrate the new season. This year his dad made
88	the guest list. He said a surprise guest would be the
99	bright spot in the party.
104	Roger got dressed in a hurry. He was so excited to
115	bake with his dad for the party that he almost
125	knocked him over in the hallway. 131

Comprehension Check

1. What time of year is the story set in? **Setting**

2. Why did Roger almost knock his dad over in the hallway?
Character

	Words Read	–	Number of Errors	=	Words Correct Score
First Read		–		=	
Second Read		–		=	

R 1.6 Read aloud fluently and accurately and with appropriate
intonation and expression.

Mice and Beans • Grade 2/Unit 4 **249**

© Macmillan/McGraw-Hill

Written directions are steps that tell you how to make or do something.

Peanut Butter and Jelly Sandwich

Ingredients: 2 slices of bread; peanut butter; jelly

Directions

1. Spread the peanut butter on one slice of bread.

2. Spread the jelly on the other slice of bread.

3. Put the slices together so the peanut butter and jelly touch.

Write a recipe for something you can make.

_____

_____

_____

_____

_____

_____

© Macmillan/McGraw-Hill

CA R 2.7 Interpret information from diagrams, charts, and graphs.

- A **contraction** is a short form of two words.
- An **apostrophe** (') takes the place of the letters that are left out of a contraction.

Read the paragraph and find the contraction and book punctuation mistakes. Rewrite the paragraph correctly on the lines below.

In the book the lives of arctic animals, I read that Arctic animals dont get cold. It isnt' just a book about animals. I also learned that the sun does'nt come out in the winter at the North Pole. Did you know that there ar'ent any trees in the Arctic?

_____

_____

_____

_____

_____

_____

Name _____

A. There are five spelling mistakes in the paragraph below. Circle the misspelled words. Write the words correctly on the lines below.

It is very cold and windy in the Arctic. You're likely to see a baby polar bear living there. You might also spot a snowy owl, but not a hauk. But it's not your fawlt. The Arctic is just too cold for some animals! Animals that have a thick coat of fur can crauwl, jump, or play in the snow. You might pawse and watch a reindeer or moose make tracks in the snow.

What other Arctic animals can you think of? Try to drauw them!

1. _____ 2. _____ 3. _____

4. _____ 5. _____

B. Writing

Write about one or more animals that can survive in the Arctic. Use five spelling words from your list.

_____

_____

_____

_____

© Macmillan/McGraw-Hill

CA **LC 1.8** Spell basic short-vowel, **long-vowel**, r-controlled, and consonant-blend patterns correctly.

Name _____

When a syllable ends in a consonant, it usually has a short vowel sound. This type of syllable is called a **closed syllable** because the vowel is "closed in" by a consonant.

pup / pet   puppet

A. Put the two syllables together. Write the word on the line. Then match the word to the picture it names.

1. mag   net _____

2. mit   ten _____

3. wal   rus _____

4. pock   et _____

B. Complete each sentence using a word from above.

5. Sandy lost her _____ in the snow.

6. I put my money in my back _____.

© Macmillan/McGraw-Hill

CA R 1.3 Decode two-syllable nonsense words and regular multisyllable words.

The Tiny Seed • Grade 2/Unit 5   **253**

Name _____

A. Match each meaning with the correct word. Write the letter of the meaning on the line.

I. burst _____

a. floats or moves along by wind

2. gently _____

b. hot, dry, sandy area of land

3. drifts _____

c. person living near another

4. drowns _____

d. to break open suddenly

5. neighbor _____

e. carefully

6. desert _____

f. covers with too much water

B. Choose two words. Use each one in a sentence. Write the sentences on the lines below.

7. _____

_____

8. _____

_____

© Macmillan/McGraw-Hill

CA R 1.0 Word Analysis, Fluency, and Systematic Vocabulary Development

Name _____

- A plural noun names more than one person, place, or thing.
- The **pronouns** *we*, *you*, and *they* can take the place of a plural noun or more than one noun or pronoun.

  <u>Rattlesnakes</u> are dangerous.   <u>They</u> are dangerous.
  <u>Emma and I</u> saw a rattlesnake.   <u>We</u> saw a rattlesnake.

Circle the correct pronoun in ( ) to complete each sentence.

1. Jamal and Nora are going to catch the snakes. We're glad (you, she) are here, Jamal and Nora!

2. Now (we, I) are safe!

3. Did you hear the wolves? (We, They) are howling.

4. Wolves don't eat people, so (we, she) are not in danger.

5. Mom and I hope to see wolf pups. (They, He) are so cute!

6. Have (you, she) ever seen a wolf pup?

7. How big does (it, they) grow?

8. (I, We) are having so much fun in the desert.

© Macmillan/McGraw-Hill

LC 1.3 Identify and correctly use various parts of speech, including nouns and verbs, in writing and speaking.

The Tiny Seed • **Grade 2/Unit 5**   **255**

Name _____

A **closed syllable** ends with a consonant. The vowel sound in a closed syllable is usually short.

can / not   cannot

Put the syllables together. Write the words. Choose the correct word to complete each sentence.

dol phin _____   rab bit _____

I. The _____ hopped away.

bas ket _____   muf fin _____

2. I had an apple and a _____ for a snack.

pic nic _____   pen cil _____

3. Dad and I had a _____ by the lake.

den tist _____   prob lem _____

4. The _____ fixed Ted's tooth.

sad ness _____   hid den _____

5. The bunny was _____ in the bushes.

© Macmillan/McGraw-Hill

 R 1.0 Word Analysis, Fluency, and Systematic Vocabulary Development

Name _____

| nap | napkin | cab | cabin | in |
| index | visit | object | cotton | happen |

A. Look at the spelling words in the box. Write the spelling words that have one closed syllable.

1. _____ 2. _____ 3. _____

Write the spelling words that have two closed syllables.

4. _____ 5. _____ 6. _____

7. _____ 8. _____ 9. _____

10. _____

B. Read each group of words. Circle the word that has two closed syllables.

11. pilot, picnic, pony

12. baby, music, cactus

13. basket, total, zebra

14. unit, open, popcorn

© Macmillan/McGraw-Hill

LC 1.8 Spell basic short-vowel, long-vowel, r-controlled, and consonant-blend patterns correctly.

As you read *The Tiny Seed*, fill in the Conclusion Chart.

Facts	Facts

Conclusion

How does the information you wrote in this Conclusion Chart help you better understand *The Tiny Seed*?

 R 2.0 Reading Comprehension

© Macmillan/McGraw-Hill

Name _____

You can use clues and what you know to help you make decisions, or **draw conclusions**, about what is happening in a story.

Draw a conclusion about each set of clues below. Write the conclusion in a sentence on the line.

1. Clues: Mike has a pair of scissors.
                    Now there are fewer flowers in the garden.

Conclusion: _____

2. Clues: Sarah had a pack of seeds.
                    The seed pack is empty now.

Conclusion: _____

3. Clues: The sky looks cloudy.
                    The ground is wet.

Conclusion: _____

4. Clues: Yesterday there was a bud on the plant.
                    Today there is a flower on the plant.

Conclusion: _____

© Macmillan/McGraw-Hill

CA **R 2.0** Reading Comprehension

Context clues are words in a sentence or a story that can help you figure out the meaning of a word you don't know. Context clues can come before or after the unfamiliar word.

Read each sentence. Look at the word in dark print. Underline the context clues that help you figure out what the word in dark print means. Then write what you think each word means.

I. With sunlight and water, a seed can **mature** into a plant.

_____

2. Tim dug a hole in the **earth** and placed the seed in it.

_____

3. The **veins** in the leaf looked like a spiderweb.

_____

4. Lisa thought the **gigantic** seed would grow into a big plant.

_____

5. Omar was so **excited** that the plant had grown that he cheered.

_____

© Macmillan/McGraw-Hill

CA R 1.0 Word Analysis, Fluency, and Systematic Vocabulary Development

Name _____

As I read, I will pay attention to my intonation.

	The raffia palm (PAHLM) has the longest leaves
7	of any plant. One leaf can be as long as a school
19	bus.
20	The leaves of the giant taro plant are also huge.
30	They look like elephant ears. But the largest leaf
39	ever is even bigger than an elephant's body!
47	A rafflesia has giant petals. These flowers can be
56	as wide as you are tall!
62	Some plants have giant seeds. The coco-de-mer
69	palm has seeds that are heavier than two bowling
78	balls. 79

Comprehension Check

1. How can you tell that the coco-de-mer seeds are heavy? **Draw Conclusions**

2. How are the plants in the passage alike? **Compare and Contrast**

	Words Read	–	Number of Errors	=	Words Correct Score
First Read		–		=	
Second Read		–		=	

R 1.6 Read aloud fluently and accurately and with appropriate intonation and expression.

The Tiny Seed • Grade 2/Unit 5   261

Name _____

> **Diagrams** are drawings that give information. **Labels** tell more about a diagram.

Look at the diagram. Read the labels. Then answer the questions below.

The Parts of a Pine Tree

Branches and **trunk** carry water and food to different parts of the tree.

Roots take water from the soil.

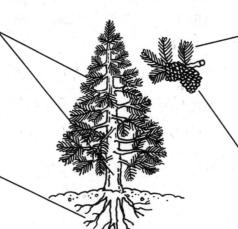

Needles make food for the tree. They stay green all year.

Cones hold the tree's seeds.

1. What does this diagram show? _____

2. Which part makes food for the tree? _____

3. What do cones do? _____

4. What carries water and food? _____

5. How does the diagram show what the roots look like?

_____

© Macmillan/McGraw-Hill

CA R 2.7 Interpret information from diagrams, charts, and graphs.

Name _____

> • A **pronoun** must agree with the noun it replaces.

Find each mistake. Then rewrite the paragraphs correctly on the lines below.

Mr. Walker taught the class what him knows about desert plants. She said, The desert is home to many plants. How can they grow in dry deserts? he asked.

Some desert plants store water in their roots, said Leah.

She are right! said Mr. Walker.

_____

_____

_____

_____

_____

© Macmillan/McGraw-Hill

LC 1.3 Identify and correctly use various parts of speech, including nouns and verbs, in writing and speaking.

A. There are six spelling mistakes in the report below. Circle the misspelled words. Write the words correctly on the lines below.

This summer I went to vissit my Aunt Sally. I flew on a plane to get there. She met me at the airport. Then she drove me to her cabbin in the woods. When I got there, I was so tired that I took a napp. When I woke up, I looked for Aunt Sally. She was inn her garden. She asked me to help her plant some seeds. "What will hapen to them?" I asked.

"I'll show you," Aunt Sally said. She opened a big book about plants. She looked in the indecks to find the page number for sunflowers. She turned to the sunflower page and showed me a picture. "When you come back in two months, they will look like this," she said.

1. _____ 2. _____ 3. _____

4. _____ 5. _____ 6. _____

B. Writing

Write a story about a trip to a community garden. Use four of the spelling words in your story.

_____

_____

_____

_____

LC 1.8 Spell basic short-vowel, long-vowel, r-controlled, and consonant-blend patterns correctly.

© Macmillan/McGraw-Hill

Name _____

Dividing a word into syllables can help you read it. When two consonants come between two vowels, you divide the word between the two consonants. These syllables are called **closed syllables**.

A. Draw a line to divide each word into syllables. Then match the word to the picture it names.

I. album

2. hammer

3. magnet

4. wallet

B. Divide each word into syllables. Then write each syllable.

5. copper

6. except

7. subject

8. blossom

_____ _____

_____ _____

_____ _____

_____ _____

© Macmillan/McGraw-Hill

CA R 1.3 Decode two-syllable nonsense words and regular multisyllable words.

A. Write the word from the box to complete each sentence.

| scent | muscles | blooming | aroma | trade | prickly |

1. The flowers are _____ and ready to pick.

2. The _____ of fresh strawberries filled the air.

3. Are your _____ strong enough to lift this crate?

4. Let's make a _____ of my tuna fish for your peanut butter and jelly sandwich.

5. The _____ from the baking cookies drew us into the kitchen.

6. A cactus is very _____.

B. Write two sentences using two words from the box.

7. _____

8. _____

© Macmillan/McGraw-Hill

CA **R 1.0** Word Analysis, Fluency, and Systematic Vocabulary Development

Name _____

> - Use **we** and **us** when you talk about yourself and another person.
> - Use **we** in the subject part of the sentence.
> - Use **us** in the predicate part.
>
>   <u>We</u> will wear tutus in the dance show.
>
>   Mom will help <u>us</u> make our costumes.

Replace the underlined words with *we* or *us*. Write the new sentence on the line below.

1. <u>Jackie and I</u> love to dance!

   _____

2. Our teacher asked <u>Jackie and me</u> to dance in the school play.

   _____

3. <u>Jackie and I</u> will learn all the steps.

   _____

4. <u>Jackie and I</u> will practice every day.

   _____

5. The audience will like <u>Jackie and me</u>.

   _____

6. They will throw roses at <u>Jackie and me</u>.

   _____

© Macmillan/McGraw-Hill

CA **LC 1.0** Written and Oral English Language Conventions

Dividing a word into syllables can help you read it. When two consonants come together between two vowels, break the word between the two consonants. These syllables are called **closed syllables**.

Draw a line to divide each word into syllables. Then write each word next to the correct clue.

kitten

problem

middle

happy

picnic

1. this comes between first and last _____

2. the opposite of *sad* _____

3. a young cat _____

4. a meal eaten outdoors _____

5. something that is difficult, or gives you trouble _____

CA R 1.3 Decode two-syllable nonsense words and regular multisyllable word

© Macmillan/McGraw-Hill

Name _____

| pen | net | publish | fuzzy | bet |
| pencil | magnet | pepper | dinner | better |

A. Word Sort

Look at the spelling words in the box. Write the spelling words that have one syllable.

1. _____   2. _____   3. _____

Write the two-syllable words that have the same two consonants in the middle.

4. _____   5. _____   6. _____   7. _____

Write the two-syllable words that have different consonants in the middle.

8. _____   9. _____   10. _____

B. Find the Pattern

Read each group of words. Circle the word that does not fit the pattern.

11. pen, net, pencil

12. dinner, bet, pepper

13. fuzzy, magnet, publish

14. tablet, better, pepper

© Macmillan/McGraw-Hill

LC 1.8 Spell basic short-vowel, long-vowel, r-controlled, and consonant-blend patterns correctly.

The Ugly Vegetables   269
Grade 2/Unit 5

Name _____

As you read *The Ugly Vegetables*, fill in the
Sequence Chart.

First

↓

Next

↓

Last

How does the information you wrote in this Sequence Chart help
you to better understand *The Ugly Vegetables*?

© Macmillan/McGraw-Hill

(CA) **R 2.0** Reading Comprehension

Name _____

The **sequence** in a story or article is the order in which the events happen.

Read the story. Then write the events in the order in which they happen.

Julie loves things that grow. She likes to take care of other people's plants when they go away. First she made a flyer. The flyer offered her services as a plant sitter. Next, she posted the flyers all around town. Then she waited for people to call. She did not have to wait long. Many people called. They were happy to have Julie take care of their plants while they were away.

First: _____

_____

Next: _____

_____

Then: _____

_____

Last: _____

_____

© Macmillan/McGraw-Hill

Homophones are words that sound the same but have different spellings and meanings. *Wait* and *weight* are homophones.

They **wait** in line to go into the movies.

The baby's **weight** was 15 pounds.

Write a word from the box to complete each sentence. Use the other words in the sentence as clues.

know	no	wood	would	weak
week	write	right	tied	tide

1. Harry will _____ a list of all the presents he wants for his birthday.

2. Do you _____ if we turn left or _____?

3. Low _____ is the best time to find shells.

4. The flu made him too _____ to play baseball.

5. The fence is made of _____.

6. I _____ like to go to the beach next _____.

© Macmillan/McGraw-Hill

CA R 1.0 Word Analysis, Fluency, and Systematic Vocabulary Development

Name _____

As I read, I will pay attention to my pronunciation of vocabulary words.

	Tomatoes are easy to grow, if there is enough water
10	and a lot of sunlight. Tomatoes need warmth. Don't plant
20	tomatoes if the weather is cold and snowy.
28	Good tomatoes need good soil. You can grow tomatoes
37	in pots or in the ground. If the pot is big enough, you can
51	leave your tomato plant in it. If it is not big enough, you
64	will need to transplant the seedling into the ground.
73	As the seedling grows taller, it grows more leaves and
83	looks like a bush. People usually tie the slightly **prickly**
93	stem to a stake. The plant climbs up the stake as it grows.
106	Next, the plant grows flowers. This is the **blooming**
115	stage. After that, the flowers turn into fruit. You will have
126	to wait about six weeks before you have ripe fruit. 136

Comprehension Check

I. What steps should you take to grow tomatoes? **Sequence**

2. Why would you choose a large pot for a tomato seedling? **Problem and Solution**

	Words Read	−	Number of Errors	=	Words Correct Score
First Read		−		=	
Second Read		−		=	

© Macmillan/McGraw-Hill

CA **R 1.6** Read aloud fluently and accurately and with appropriate intonation and expression.

Name _____

Written directions are steps that tell how to make or do something.

A. These directions are out of order. Write them in order on the lines below.

After filling the celery, sprinkle raisins on the cream cheese.

Wash and dry a stalk of celery.

Then gently press the raisins into the cheese.

Fill the hollow part of the celery with cream cheese.

I. _____

_____

2. _____

_____

3. _____

_____

4. _____

_____

B. This snack is called *Ants on a Log*. Circle the picture that shows the snack.

© Macmillan/McGraw-Hill

CA R 2.1 Use titles, tables of contents, and chapter headings to locate information in expository text.

Name _____

- Use **I** and **we** in the subject of a sentence.

- Use **me** and **us** in the predicate part of a sentence.

- The pronoun **I** is always a capital letter.

- Name yourself last when talking about yourself and another person.

Circle each mistake in the use of pronouns. Then rewrite the paragraph correctly on the lines below.

Mom and me went to see a musical. The usher gave i a program and showed we where to sit. Us had great seats! i could see the actors right up close. i hope Mom takes I to another show soon!

_____

_____

_____

_____

_____

© Macmillan/McGraw-Hill

Name _____

A. There are six spelling mistakes in the paragraph below. Circle the misspelled words. Write the words correctly on the lines below.

     Mark and his dad worked in the garden. Mark was tired of the garden. He thought the vegetables would never grow. Then one day, he saw something green. It was a big green peper! Mark's dad broke off a piece. They each took a bite. It tasted good. It was beter than the ones from the store. Mark's family ate the rest of it for dinnir. Mark wanted to write a letter to his grandfather to tell him about the garden. Mark looked for a penn. He could only find a pensil. He wrote, "I bett you would like to see it."

1. _____ 2. _____ 3. _____

4. _____ 5. _____ 6. _____

B. Writing

Write about something you grew or made. Use four words from your spelling list.

_____

_____

_____

_____

CA **LC 1.8** Spell basic short-vowel, long-vowel, r-controlled, and consonant-blend patterns correctly.

© Macmillan/McGraw-Hill

Name _____

Dividing a word into syllables can help you read it. When a consonant comes between two vowels, you usually divide the word before the consonant. The vowel in the first syllable has a long vowel sound. For example, you would divide the word *pilot* into the syllables *pi-* and *-lot*. The syllable *pi-* is called an **open syllable** because it isn't closed in by a consonant.

A. Draw a line to divide each word into syllables. Then match the word to the picture it names.

1. donut

2. crayon

3. zebra

4. pony

B. Divide each word into syllables. Then write each syllable.

5. broken   **7.** music

R 1.3 Decode two-syllable nonsense words and regular multisyllable words.

Meet the Super Croc   **277**
Grade 2/Unit 5

© Macmillan/McGraw-Hill

A. Write words from the box to complete the story.

site	hopeful	unable	confirm	ancient	valid

Sasha found a little bone in her yard. The bone was covered in

dirt as if it had been at that _____ for many years.

It looked _____. Maybe it was a dinosaur bone!

"Let's try to _____ what it is," Dad said. They
looked at pictures in dinosaur books. They tried and tried but

were _____ to find a bone that looked like the one
Sasha had found. Sasha still thought it was a dinosaur bone. Dad

said, "Your idea might be _____. Or maybe you
found a chicken bone from a picnic last summer!"

B. Use a word from the box to add another sentence to the story.

_____

_____

(CA) **R 1.0** Word Analysis, Fluency, and Systematic Vocabulary Development

© Macmillan/McGraw-Hill

- A **possessive pronoun** shows who or what owns something. Some possessive pronouns are ***its, our, your,*** and ***their***.

  <u>Our</u> house is on Elm Street.   <u>Their</u> house is on Oak Street.

  <u>Your</u> house is pretty.   <u>Its</u> color is pink.

Underline the correct possessive pronouns. Write the sentences correctly on the lines.

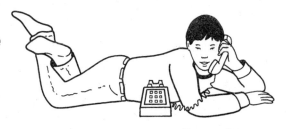

I. (Us, Our) class is learning about Alexander Graham Bell and Thomas Watson.

_____

2. (Their, They) invention changed the way we live.

_____

3. Can you imagine (your, our) life without a telephone?

_____

4. (It's, Its) technology helps us to stay in touch.

_____

5. What inventor will (our, its) teacher tell us about next?

_____

6. What is (your, you're) favorite invention?

_____

© Macmillan/McGraw-Hill

When a consonant comes between two vowels, divide the word before the consonant. The vowel in the first syllable will usually have a long vowel sound. For example, you would divide the word *tiger* into the syllables *ti-* and *-ger*. The syllable *ti-* is an **open syllable**.

A. Draw a line to divide each word into syllables. Then complete each sentence below with the correct word.

1. moment

2. decide

3. hero

4. student

5. photo

B. Use the words above to complete each sentence below.

6. I am a _____ in second grade.

7. Then one day, I _____ to help a boy find his lost dog.

8. In just one _____, I become a special person.

9. Now I am a _____.

10. A _____ of the boy, his dog, and me is hanging in school.

© Macmillan/McGraw-Hill

CA R 1.3 Decode two-syllable nonsense words and regular multisyllable words.

Name _____

| human | lady | crazy | gravy | open |
| giant | lazy | navy | solo | odor |

A. Word Sort

Look at the spelling words in the box. Match each word to the long vowel sound in its open syllable. Write the spelling words on the lines below.

long *a*

1. _____
2. _____
3. _____
4. _____
5. _____

long *o*

6. _____
7. _____
8. _____

long *i*

9. _____

long *u*

10. _____

B. Missing Letter

A vowel is missing from each spelling word below. Write the missing letter in the box. Then write the spelling word correctly on the line.

11. cr ☐ zy _____

12. ☐ dor _____

13. h ☐ man _____

14. g ☐ ant _____

© Macmillan/McGraw-Hill

LC 1.8 Spell basic short-vowel, long-vowel, r-controlled, and consonant-blend patterns correctly.

Meet the Super Croc   281
Grade 2/Unit 5

As you read *Meet the Super Croc*, fill in the Summary Chart.

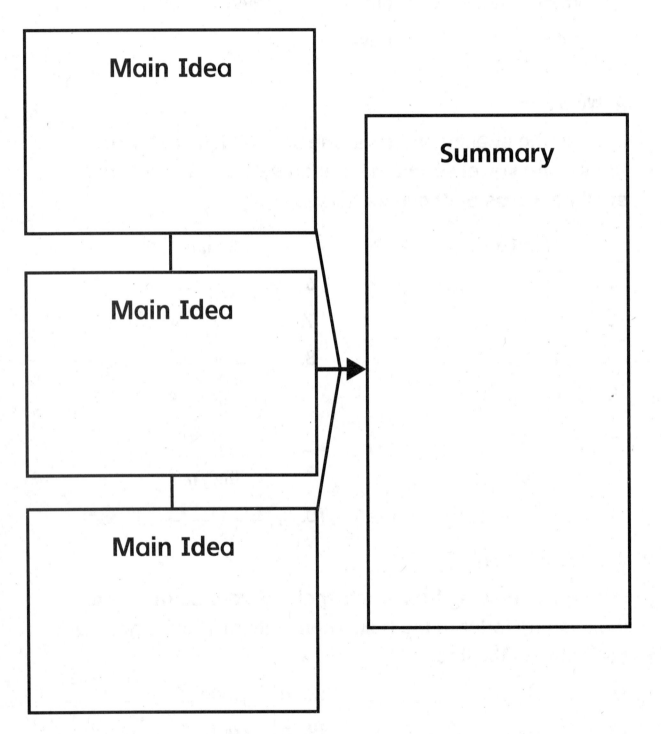

How does the information you wrote in this Summary Chart help you to better understand *Meet the Super Croc*?

© Macmillan/McGraw-Hill

CA R 2.0 Reading Comprehension

Name _____

Use the main idea and details of a story to help you **summarize** what you read.

Read the passage. Then follow the directions.

Spiders can grow new legs if their legs get hurt or lost. Lizards can grow new tails. Sharks lose thousands of teeth in their lives, but don't worry, they also grow thousands of new ones. These are just a few of many animals that can grow new parts.

1. What is the main idea of this paragraph?

   a. Some animals can grow whole new animals.

   b. Some animals lose thousands of teeth.

   c. Some animals can grow new body parts.

2. Choose two details that tell about the main idea.

   a. Lizards can grow new tails.

   b. There are other animals that can grow whole new animals from body parts.

   c. Spiders can grow new legs.

3. Choose one detail that does not tell about the main idea.

   a. Sharks lose thousands of teeth but can grow them back.

   b. If a spider loses a leg, it can grow it back.

   c. Whole animals can sometimes grow from a part of another animal.

4. Write a good title that summarizes this passage.

_____

© Macmillan/McGraw-Hill

 R 2.0 Reading Comprehension

Name _____

A word part that is added to the end of a word to change its meaning is called a **suffix**. A word part that is added to the beginning of a word to change its meaning is called a **prefix**.

Suffixes

-ful = "full of"

-less = "without"

re- = "again"

un- = "not"

dis- = "do the opposite of"

Complete each sentence with a new word made from one of the base words and one of the prefixes or suffixes below. Use any word part more than once if you need to.

Prefixes:		Base words:		Suffixes:
re- un- dis-	**+**	use care visit like	**+**	-ful -less

I. A raccoon was at our campsite last night and it may

_____ us tonight.

2. This dinosaur book is very _____ to our class.

3. I _____ burned toast.

4. The peacock's tail is _____ any other bird's tail.

5. It was _____ of you to let the dog out.

CA R 1.9 Know the meaning of simple prefixes and suffixes (e.g., *over-*, *un-*, *-ing*, *-ly*).

© Macmillan/McGraw-Hill

Name _____

As I read, I will pay attention to phrasing and pronunciation.

	Have you ever seen a living dinosaur? Of course
9	not! Dinosaurs are extinct. They no longer exist.
17	All of the dinosaurs died out about 65 million years
26	ago. No one really knows why. Some scientists think
35	it was because Earth's climate changed.
41	Many other animals are also extinct. Some
48	became extinct in **ancient** times. Others became
55	extinct less than 100 years ago. Let's learn about
63	some of them.
66	The woolly mammoth looked like an elephant.
73	But woolly mammoths were even bigger!
79	Like elephants, woolly mammoths had tusks and a
87	trunk. Unlike elephants, they had long, shaggy hair
95	all over their bodies. Woolly mammoths lived during
103	the Ice Age. Their long hair kept them warm. 112

Comprehension Check

1. What does it mean for an animal to be extinct? **Summarize**

2. How were woolly mammoths like elephants? **Main Idea and Details**

	Words Read	−	Number of Errors	=	Words Correct Score
First Read		−		=	
Second Read		−		=	

© Macmillan/McGraw-Hill

CA R 1.6 Read aloud fluently and accurately and with appropriate intonation and expression.

Meet the Super Croc
Grade 2/Unit 5   285

Name _____

Before you write a report, you need to choose a topic. You need to **narrow the topic** until it is small enough to cover in the space you have. Plan to focus on just one or two main ideas so your topic is not too big.

A. Read the sentences below. Then answer the questions.

Liam has to research and write a one-page report about an animal. He plans to write about mammals.

I. Is Liam's topic idea a good one for his report? Why or why not?

_____

_____

B. Write three examples of better topic ideas for Liam.

2. _____ **3.** _____

4. _____

5. Tell why your ideas would work well for Liam's report.

_____

_____

_____

© Macmillan/McGraw-Hill

CA R 2.0 Reading Comprehension

Description Writing Frame

Summarize *Meet the Super Croc.*
Use the Description Writing Frame below.

The super croc is an interesting animal.

One interesting fact about this animal is _____

_____

_____.

A second interesting fact about this animal is _____

_____

_____.

A third interesting fact about this animal is _____

_____

_____.

A fourth interesting fact about this animal is _____

_____

_____.

**Rewrite the completed summary on another sheet of paper.
Keep it as a model for writing a summary of an article or
selection using this text structure.**

© Macmillan/McGraw-Hill

- A **possessive pronoun** takes the place of a possessive noun.

- A possessive pronoun shows who or what owns something. Some possessive pronouns are *my, your, his, its, our, your,* and *their*.

- A proper noun begins with a capital letter.

- The name of a day, month, or holiday begins with a capital letter.

Find the mistakes. Rewrite the paragraph correctly on the lines below.

Me twin brothers have a birthday on presidents' day. There party is on saturday, february 18. Us parents got the boys a puppy as a present. Their name is gus. Gus will sleep in them room.

_____

_____

_____

_____

_____

© Macmillan/McGraw-Hill

Name _____

A. Proofreading Activity

**There are five spelling mistakes in the report below.
Circle the misspelled words. Write the words correctly
on the lines below.**

   Long ago, dinosaurs lived on Earth. Some of them were
as big as a gient. Others were tiny. No humin being has
seen a real dinosaur. But they have seen models of them.
Scientists found dinosaur bones. They put the bones
together to make a model. They didn't work sollo to do
this. They had to work together. They also couldn't be
lazie. They had to work hard. Some people thought it was
a crazey idea. But it worked!

I. _____   4. _____

2. _____   5. _____

3. _____

B. Writing Activity

**On another sheet of paper, write a short story about an
animal that lives today. Use four of the spelling words in
your story.**

CA LC 1.8 Spell basic short-vowel, long-vowel, r-controlled, and
consonant-blend patterns correctly.

Meet the Super Croc   **289**
Grade 2/Unit 5

Name _____

> When a word ends in **-le**, the consonant before it plus the letters **le** form the last syllable. This is called a **consonant + le syllable**.

A. Draw a line to divide each word into syllables. Then match the word to the picture it names.

I. needle

2. marble

3. table

4. saddle

B. Put a word part from the box with each word part below to make a word. Write the word on the line.

zle	tle	kle	ple

5. pur _____ 7. puz _____

6. lit _____ 8. wrin _____

 R 1.3 Decode two-syllable nonsense words and regular multisyllable words.

© Macmillan/McGraw-Hill

Name _____

A. Write the word from the box that matches each clue.

| peered giggled snuggled fluttered vanished recognized |

1. This word means "held something close" or "cuddled."

   _____

2. This word means "disappeared" or "went out of sight."

   _____

3. This word means "laughed in a silly way."

   _____

4. This word means "knew by sight."

   _____

5. This word means "flew with quick flapping movements."

   _____

6. This word means "looked closely."

   _____

B. Choose two words from the box. Then write a sentence for each word that you chose on the lines.

7. _____

8. _____

© Macmillan/McGraw-Hill

Name _____

- A **contraction** is a short form of two words put together.
- An apostrophe (') takes the place of the missing letter or letters in the contraction.

it is	it's	we are	we're
they are	they're	you are	you're

Write the contraction for the underlined words.
Write the new sentence on the line below.

1. It is a starry night. _____

_____

2. We are gazing at the stars. _____

_____

3. They are beautiful! _____

_____

4. It is going to be nice tomorrow. _____

_____

5. You are reading books about stars. _____

_____

CA LC 1.0 Written and Oral English Language Conventions

© Macmillan/McGraw-Hill

When a word ends in **-le**, the consonant before it plus the letters **le** form the last syllable. This is called a **consonant + le syllable**.

Divide each word into syllables. Write each syllable on the line. Then write each word next to the correct clue.

1. rattle   _____   _____

2. puddle   _____   _____

3. pebble   _____   _____

4. jungle   _____   _____

5. circle   _____   _____

6. a place where wild animals live _____

7. a small rock or stone _____

8. a small pool of water on the ground _____

9. a round shape _____

10. a baby's toy _____

© Macmillan/McGraw-Hill

R 1.3 Decode two-syllable nonsense words and regular multisyllable words.

Farfallina and Marcel
Grade 2/Unit 5   **293**

Name _____

lit	set	rip	pad	middle
little	settle	ripple	paddle	bubble

A. Word Sort

Look at the spelling words in the box. Write the spelling words that have one syllable. Then write the words that have two syllables.

one syllable

1. _____

2. _____

3. _____

4. _____

two syllables

5. _____

6. _____

7. _____

8. _____

9. _____

10. _____

B. Rhyme Time

Write the spelling words that rhyme with each of these words.

11. slip _____

12. saddle _____

13. wet _____

14. riddle _____

CA **LC 1.8** Spell basic short-vowel, long-vowel, *r*-controlled, and consonant-blend patterns correctly.

© Macmillan/McGraw-Hill

Name _____

**As you read *Farfallina and Marcel*, fill in the
Inferences Chart.**

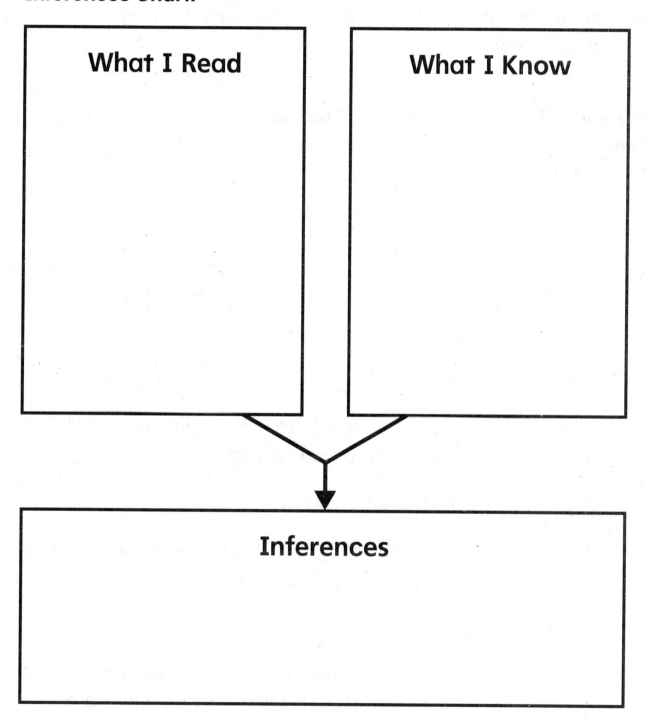

What I Read	What I Know

Inferences

How does the information you wrote in this Inferences Chart
help you generate questions about *Farfallina and Marcel*?

© Macmillan/McGraw-Hill

Name _____

When you **make inferences**, you use what you already
know and what you have read to figure out something
about a story.

**Read each set of sentences. Then answer
each question to make an inference.**

1. The kittens met Mary at the door. Then they
   ran over to their food bowls and meowed loudly.

   What do the kittens want? _____

2. Ty stored his shorts, T-shirts, and bathing suit in a chest. He
   took out his sweaters and long pants.

   What time of year is it? _____

3. All the kids lined up. Max yelled, "Go!" Everyone ran fast. Amy
   won. "That's my sister, Amy!" Max yelled.

   How does Max feel about his sister? _____

4. Janet sneezed. Then she coughed. Dad felt her forehead. "You
   feel hot. I think you'd better go back to bed."

   How is Janet feeling? _____

5. Mr. Night milked the cows. Then he gathered eggs from the hen
   house. After that he plowed the fields and planted the corn.

   Where does Mr. Night work? _____

© Macmillan/McGraw-Hill

CA R 2.0 Reading Comprehension

Name _____

> **Synonyms** are words that have the same or almost the same meaning.

Use the dictionary and thesaurus entries to answer the questions. Then circle the source you used.

Dictionary	Thesaurus
trash (trash) *noun* something you throw away **trip** (trip) **1.** *noun* to go from one place to another. **2.** *verb* you hit your foot on something and almost fall	**trash:** garbage, junk, rubbish **trip:** *noun* drive, ride, journey *verb* fall, slip, stumble

I. What does **trash** mean? _____

   dictionary   thesaurus

2. What is a synonym for the verb **trip**? _____

   dictionary   thesaurus

3. What does the noun **trip** mean? _____

   dictionary   thesaurus

4. What are two synonyms for **trash**? _____

   dictionary   thesaurus

 R 1.7 Understand and explain common antonyms and synonyms.

As I read, I will pay attention to the expression and phrasing in each sentence.

	My name is Hermie. My mother was a land hermit
10	crab. She laid her eggs on the wet rocks next to the sea.
23	When I hatched, I floated in the warm ocean. I saw
34	many other baby hermit crabs there. That is where I met
45	my friend Harriet.
48	As we grew, we molted. We slipped out of the hard
59	skin around our body.
63	When we had molted for the last time, we knew it was
75	time to swim to shore.
80	Our lungs were changing. Soon we would only be able
90	to breathe air. 93

Comprehension Check

1. What happens to a crab when it molts? **Main Idea and Details**

2. Where will Hermie live after his lungs change? **Draw Conclusions**

	Words Read	–	Number of Errors	=	Words Correct Score
First Read		–		=	
Second Read		–		=	

© Macmillan/McGraw-Hill

CA R 1.6 Read aloud fluently and accurately and with appropriate intonation and expression.

Name _____

Captions are the words below a picture. They tell what the picture is about.

Match each caption to a picture. Write the letter in the box. Then write a different caption for each picture on the line below.

a. Go that way.   b. This is a painting.

c. We have fun.   d. This is a kitten.

I.  ☐

_____

_____

2.  ☐

_____

_____

3.  ☐

_____

_____

4.  ☐

_____

_____

© Macmillan/McGraw-Hill

CA R 2.7 Interpret information from diagrams, charts, and graphs.

Farfallina and Marcel
Grade 2/Unit 5   **299**

- An apostrophe (') takes the place of the letters left out of a contraction.
- Possessive pronouns do not have apostrophes.
- The present-tense verb must agree with a pronoun in the subject part of a sentence.

Rewrite the paragraph correctly on the lines.

Were learning about the moon. Mr. Jones know a lot about the moon. Hes an expert! He say the moon cannot be seen at the start of it's cycle. Its called the New Moon.

_____

_____

_____

_____

_____

_____

© Macmillan/McGraw-Hill

A. There are six spelling mistakes in the story below. Circle the misspelled words. Write the words correctly on the lines below.

Two frogs sat on a lily padd. They talked about when they were litle tadpoles. The first frog said, "I couldn't paddel in the pond."

The other frog said, "I couldn't swim to the middul."

The first frog said, "Now I can dive. And I can make a buble."

The frogs jumped off the pad. They made a rippel in the water. Then they swam off.

I. _____   4. _____

2. _____   5. _____

3. _____   6. _____

B. Writing

Write about something you can do that you couldn't do when you were younger. Use four words from your spelling list.

_____

_____

_____

_____

© Macmillan/McGraw-Hill

LC 1.8 Spell basic short-vowel, long-vowel, *r*-controlled, and consonant-blend patterns correctly.

Farfallina and Marcel
Grade 2/Unit 5

301

Name _____

When a syllable ends in a vowel, the vowel sound is usually long. This type of syllable is called an **open syllable**.

For example, the first syllable in the word *lilac* is *lī*. The syllable *lī* is an open syllable and the sound of the vowel *i* is long.

A. Put the two syllables together to make a word. Write the word on the line. Then match the word to the picture it names.

1. spi   der _____

2. ze   bra _____

3. po   ny _____

4. a   corn _____

B. Divide each word into syllables. Write each syllable on the line.

5. even

7. silent

_____ • _____   _____ • _____

6. soda

8. cable

_____ • _____   _____ • _____

CA R 1.3 Decode two-syllable nonsense words and regular multisyllable words.

© Macmillan/McGraw-Hill

Name _____

Choose the word from the box to complete each sentence. Then write the word on the line.

| glanced beloved promised noble gleamed wiggled |

1. Aunt Linda lives in a farmhouse with her _____ pigs, Princess and Queeny.

2. I _____ to visit when school lets out for the summer.

3. I _____ at the pictures of my last visit to her farm.

4. Queeny wore a diamond collar that _____ in the light.

5. Princess _____ around in mud to keep cool.

6. Although pigs like to roll around in the mud, I think they are very

_____ animals.

© Macmillan/McGraw-Hill

Name _____

- Remember that a present-tense verb must agree with its pronoun subject.

- With the pronouns *I, we, you,* and *they*, do **not** add *-s* to most action verbs to form the present tense.

  <u>We visit</u> your garden.   <u>You show</u> us around.

  <u>I pick</u> some tomatoes.   <u>They taste</u> great!

Circle the pronoun in ( ) that agrees with the verb in each sentence.

1. (You, She) enjoy gardening.

2. (We, He) think your garden is lovely.

3. What kind of flowers do (you, she) grow?

4. (I, He) see red roses.

5. (It, They) grow so tall!

6. How do (she, you) grow such pretty flowers?

7. (I, He) want to take some flowers home.

8. Can (we, us) pick the roses?

© Macmillan/McGraw-Hill

Name _____

When a syllable ends in a vowel, the vowel sound is usually long. This type of syllable is called an **open syllable**. The first syllable in *robot* is *rō*. The syllable *rō* is an open syllable and the sound of the vowel *o* is long.

Divide each word into syllables. Write each syllable on the line. Then write the correct word to answer each riddle.

1. over   _____   _____

2. zero   _____   _____

3. before   _____   _____

4. tuna   _____   _____

5. paper   _____   _____

6. I am the opposite of "after." What am I? _____

7. I am a kind of fish. What am I? _____

8. I am something you write on. What am I? _____

9. I am the numeral that is less than one. What am I?

_____

10. I am the opposite of "under." What am I? _____

© Macmillan/McGraw-Hill

CA   **R 1.3** Decode two-syllable nonsense words and regular multisyllable words.

Nutik, the Wolf Pup • **Grade 2/Unit 5**   **305**

Name _____

| no | male | baby | bacon | return |
| noble | female | basic | relate | lion |

A. Word Sort

Look at the spelling words in the box. Match each word
to the long vowel sound in its open syllable. Write the
spelling words on the lines below.

long a

1. _____

2. _____

3. _____

long i

4. _____

long e

5. _____

6. _____

7. _____

long o

8. _____

9. _____

B. Missing Letter

The vowel is missing from each spelling word below.
Write the missing letter in the box. Then write the spelling
word correctly on the line.

10. r [ ] turn _____   11. b [ ] by _____

12. n [ ] ble _____   13. b [ ] con _____

14. l [ ] on _____

© Macmillan/McGraw-Hill

CA **LC 1.8** Spell basic short-vowel, long-vowel, r-controlled,
and consonant-blend patterns correctly.

As you read *Nutik, the Wolf Pup*, fill in the Inferences Chart.

What I Read	What I Know

My Inferences

How does the information you wrote in this Inferences Chart
help you to better understand *Nutik, the Wolf Pup*?

© Macmillan/McGraw-Hill

When you **make inferences**, you make decisions about a story based on what you already know and clues from the story.

Read the story. Then answer the questions.

Hebert hummed as he unlocked the door to his shop. Yesterday was his first day as a shopkeeper, and it hadn't gone well. He hadn't sold anything. But he was sure today would be different! His idea to sell bottled ice water was sure to take off. He tipped his head back and looked at the bright sun. It made the polar seas and icebergs that surrounded his shop gleam. Perfect! He stretched his wings and smoothed his feathers with his beak. Waddling into the store, he began to tidy the shelves lined with frozen bottles of water. He was sure that customers would be coming soon.

I. What time of day do you think it is? What clues did you use?

_____

_____

2. What clues do you have that Hebert is not a human?

_____

3. What kind of animal do you think Hebert is?

_____

4. What do you think is wrong with Hebert's plan?

_____

© Macmillan/McGraw-Hill

CA **R 2.0** Reading Comprehension

Name _____

A **verb** is an action word. To show that action takes place in the past, **-*ed*** is added to the verb.

Underline the verb in each sentence. Then change each verb so that it tells about the past. Write the new word on the line.

1. The turtles walk slowly on their short legs. _____

2. The rabbits munch on grass and leaves. _____

3. The fox cubs watch their mother. _____

4. The chipmunks climb into a hollow log. _____

5. Two frogs hop onto a lily pad. _____

6. The kittens play with the ball of string. _____

7. The bears want the camper's food. _____

8. The robins collect twigs for their nest. _____

© Macmillan/McGraw-Hill

As I read, I will pay attention to tone and expression.

	A coral reef is like a big city under the water. Thousands
12	of sea creatures live around a coral reef.
20	Coral reefs grow in shallow, warm seas. They grow all
30	over the world.
33	Tiny animals called polyps (*PAHL-ips*) build corals. Each
40	polyp makes a hard coral cup to use as a home. Millions of
53	cups form a coral reef.
58	Corals come in all shapes and sizes. Staghorn coral looks
68	like spiky purple antlers. Plate coral looks like a large dinner
79	plate. Brain coral looks like a big brain.
87	Fish love coral reefs because there is plenty of food.
97	Parrotfish crunch on the coral with their sharp teeth.
106	Lionfish have red and white stripes. They also have long
116	fins and spines. Lionfish use their long spines to trap small
127	fish against the coral. 131

Comprehension Check

1. Why do fish love coral reefs? **Make Inferences**

2. How are coral reefs like big underwater cities? **Make and Confirm Predictions**

	Words Read	–	Number of Errors	=	Words Correct Score
First Read		–		=	
Second Read		–		=	

© Macmillan/McGraw-Hill

 R 1.6 Read aloud fluently and accurately and with appropriate intonation and expression.

Name _____

A. **Suppose you have a research assignment. You have to write a one-page paper on one animal. Think about this assignment as you answer each question below.**

1. Circle the topic that best fits the assignment.

   arctic animals   polar bears   fish

2. Which reference material would be the best one to use?

   encyclopedia   dictionary   atlas

3. Why is your choice the best reference material for the assignment?

   _____

   _____

   _____

B. **The encyclopedia article on your animal has sections with the following heads:**

   Appearance   Habitat   Diet

4. In which section would you find information about what your animal eats? _____

5. Which section may include a photo of your animal?

   _____

6. Which section may include a map that shows where your animal lives? _____

© Macmillan/McGraw-Hill

CA **R 2.1** Use titles, tables of contents, and chapter headings to locate information in expository text.

- With the pronouns *he*, *she*, and *it*, add *-s* to most action verbs to form the present tense.

- With the pronouns *I*, *we*, *you*, and *they*, do **not** add *-s* to most action verbs to form the present tense.

- Begin the first word and all the important words in a book title with capital letters.

- Underline all the words in a book title.

Find the mistakes. Rewrite the paragraph correctly.

Mom and I goes to the library. She read <u>how to grow a garden</u>. I reads A Kid's Guide to Gardening. The books tells us how to grow a garden. We wants to plant flowers. We knows it take hard work.

_____

_____

_____

_____

_____

© Macmillan/McGraw-Hill

CA **LC 1.0** Written and Oral English Language Conventions

A. There are six spelling mistakes in the report below. Circle the misspelled words. Write the words correctly on the lines below.

Do you know why the lyon is called the "king of the jungle?" I think it is because these animals are such nobule creatures. These animals like to live in groups, called prides. The mayl protects the pride by guarding the area. The femayl does most of the hunting. If she has a babie, called a cub, she takes care of it. She teaches it baysic skills, like how to hunt.

1. _____   3. _____   5. _____

2. _____   4. _____   6. _____

B. Writing Activity

Write a short report about a wild animal. Use four of the spelling words in your report.

© Macmillan/McGraw-Hill

LC 1.8 Spell basic short-vowel, long-vowel, r-controlled, and consonant-blend patterns correctly.

Nutik, the Wolf Pup • Grade 2/Unit 5   313

Name _____

When a word ends in -*le*, the consonant before it plus the letters -*le* form the last syllable. This is called a **consonant + *le* syllable**.

Example: **table**　**ta**　open syllable　+　**ble**
　　　　　consonant + *le* syllable
　　　　　candle　**can**　closed syllable　+　**dle**
　　　　　consonant + *le* syllable

A. Put the two syllables together. Write the word. Then match the word to the picture it names.

I. bee　tle _____

2. bu　gle _____

3. whis　tle _____

4. stee　ple _____

B. Complete each sentence with a word you made. Write the correct word on the line.

5. The cowboy wants a new _____ for his horse.

6. Did the umpire blow his _____?

© Macmillan/McGraw-Hill

CA　R 1.3　Decode two-syllable nonsense words and regular multisyllable words.

Name _____

**Choose a word from the box to finish each sentence.
Then write the word on the line.**

| lengthy | beyond | burrow | warning | distant |

1. Mark ran so quickly that he ran _____ the finish line.

2. Scientists study _____ stars and planets.

3. Many desert animals can spend _____ periods of time without water.

4. There was a _____ to all hikers to stay inside because of the sandstorm.

5. A desert tortoise can dig an underground _____ to escape the heat.

© Macmillan/McGraw-Hill

Name _____

- An **adjective** is a word that describes a noun.
- Some adjectives tell how many.

Circle the adjectives that tell how many. Then rewrite each sentence using a new amount.

1. My birthday is in three weeks.

_____

2. I am inviting ten friends to my party.

_____

3. Mom is blowing up a few balloons.

_____

4. There will be nine candles on my cake.

_____

5. One candle is for good luck.

_____

6. There will be many sweet treats.

_____

© Macmillan/McGraw-Hill

LC 1.0 Written and Oral English Language Conventions

Name _____

When a word ends in **-le**, the consonant before it plus the letters **-le** form the last syllable. This is called a **consonant + le syllable**. Words with both open and closed syllables can end in a consonant + **le** syllable.

A. Put a word part from the box with each word part below to make a word. Write the word on the line.

kle	cle	tle	ple	gle	ble

I. ca   + _____ = _____

2. mus   + _____ = _____

3. twin   + _____ = _____

4. wig   + _____ = _____

5. ma   + _____ = _____

6. whis   + _____ = _____

B. Use a word that you made to answer each riddle below. Write each word on the line.

7. I am part of your body. I help you run, skip, and jump. I help make you strong. What am I?

_____

8. I am something you blow in to make a noise. Umpires and coaches sometimes use me. What am I?

_____

© Macmillan/McGraw-Hill

R 1.3 Decode two-syllable nonsense words and regular multisyllable words.

Dig, Wait, Listen • **Grade 2/Unit 6**   **317**

Name _____

| rat | rid | sad | jig | apple |
| rattle | riddle | saddle | jiggle | puddle |

A. Word Sort

Look at the spelling words in the box. Write the spelling words that have one syllable. Then write the words that have two syllables.

One Syllable

1. _____
2. _____
3. _____
4. _____

Two Syllables

5. _____
6. _____
7. _____
8. _____
9. _____
10. _____

B. Rhyme Time

Write the spelling words that rhyme with each of these words.

11. had

_____

12. middle

_____

13. cattle

_____

14. giggle

_____

15. cuddle

_____

16. cat

_____

© Macmillan/McGraw-Hill

CA **LC 1.8** Spell basic short-vowel, long-vowel, *r*-controlled, and consonant-blend patterns correctly.

Name _____

As you read *Dig, Wait, Listen: A Desert Toad's Tale*, fill in the
Author's Purpose Chart.

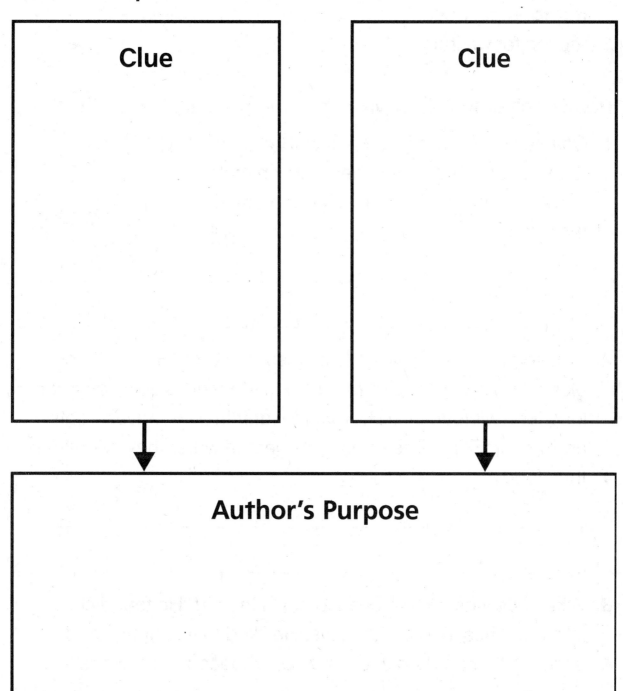

Clue	Clue

Author's Purpose

How does the information you wrote in this Author's Purpose Chart
help you summarize *Dig, Wait, Listen: A Desert Toad's Tale*?

© Macmillan/McGraw-Hill

R 2.0 Reading Comprehension

Name _____

One way to summarize a selection is to think about the **author's purpose**. The author's purpose is the writer's reason for writing.

Read each story. Then write the author's purpose on the lines.

1. Coyotes make different sounds. They howl to talk to other coyotes. They yelp when they play, and they bark when they are protecting their den.

_____

_____

2. A desert is a dry habitat. It gets less rain in a year than most plants and animals need to live. Some desert plants can live a long time without rain. They store water in their leaves, roots, and stems. Some desert animals get the water they need from their food.

_____

_____

3. When Joe was six, he loved to dig in the dirt. He found coins, tree branches, and broken toys. He liked to find things and examine them. When Joe grew up, he became a scientist.

_____

_____

© Macmillan/McGraw-Hill

CA R 2.0 Reading Comprehension

Name _____

A word that shows who or what owns something is a **possessive** noun. Many possessive nouns are formed by adding an apostrophe (') and *s*.

Choose the possessive from the box that best completes the sentence. Then write it on the line.

> giraffe's   teacher's   dad's   bird's   dentist's   rabbit's

1. I borrowed chalk from the _____ desk.

2. Two eggs were in the _____ nest.

3. I waited to get my teeth checked at the _____ office.

4. The fox tried to enter the _____ burrow.

5. I used my _____ tools to fix my toy car.

6. Can you believe how long

the _____ neck is?

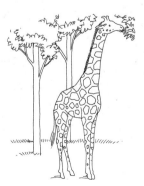

© Macmillan/McGraw-Hill

Name _____

As I read, I will pay attention to intonation.

	Australia is the driest continent in the world. It has
10	ten deserts.
12	All deserts are very dry. They are hot during the day and
24	cold at night. But many plants and animals have adapted to
35	life in the desert.
39	People live in the Australian desert, too. The Aboriginal
48	[ab-uh-RIJ-i-nuhl] people have lived in the Australian
54	desert for 40,000 years.
57	The red kangaroo lives in the Australian desert. A female
67	can carry its young in a pouch, or pocket, on its stomach.
79	Kangaroos are marsupials. There are more than 200
86	kinds of marsupials that live in or near Australia.
95	Most desert marsupials, such as the numbat, are small. They
105	can dig into the sand and hide under rocks or in trees. 117

Comprehension Check

1. What does the author want you to know? **Author's Purpose**

2. How is Australia different from all other continents? **Compare and Contrast**

	Words Read	–	Number of Errors	=	Words Correct Score
First Read		–		=	
Second Read		–		=	

© Macmillan/McGraw-Hill

CA R 1.6 Read aloud fluently and accurately and with appropriate **intonation** and expression.

A **chart** gives information in a clear way. Information is often organized under headings. It is often easier to read facts in a chart than in a paragraph.

Use the information from the chart to answer the questions.

Desert Spadefoot Toads		
Where They Are Found	**Characteristics**	**Other Facts**
Sonoran Desert	olive gray to brown color	eat insects
underground	pale belly	nocturnal
on land or in water	short limbs	lay eggs
	amphibian	

1. In which desert can you find the spadefoot toad? _____

2. What color are the spadefoot toads? _____

3. What do they eat? _____

4. How would you describe the limbs of the toads?

_____

© Macmillan/McGraw-Hill

CA R 2.7 Interpret information from diagrams, charts, and graphs.

Dig, Wait, Listen • **Grade 2/Unit 6** 323

- Use commas to separate three or more items in a series.
- An apostrophe takes the place of letters left out of a contraction.
- The present-tense verb must agree with a pronoun in the subject part of a sentence.

Find the mistakes. Rewrite the paragraph correctly on the lines.

Were throwing a surprise party for Maria Anna and Louisa. Their triplets! We'll serve sandwiches juice potato chips and chocolate cake. Were sure theyll be surprised.

_____

_____

_____

_____

_____

_____

CA LC 1.0 Written and Oral English Language Conventions

© Macmillan/McGraw-Hill

A. There are six spelling mistakes in the story below. Circle the misspelled words. Write the words correctly on the lines below.

Can you guess my ridle? I'm thinking of an animal. It will not eat an appul. But it might eat a raat. It doesn't wear a saddel, so it's not a horse. It won't do a jigg, so it's not a pig. Can you guess yet? Here's another clue. This animal slithers on the ground and makes the sound of a ratel. Now you can guess: It's a snake!

1. _____   3. _____   5. _____

2. _____   4. _____   6. _____

B. Writing

Write a riddle story about an animal that lives in a desert, a jungle, or a pond. Use four words from your spelling list. Circle the spelling words you use.

_____

_____

_____

_____

_____

_____

_____

© Macmillan/McGraw-Hill

LC 1.8 Spell basic short-vowel, long-vowel, *r*-controlled, and consonant-blend patterns correctly.

Dig, Wait, Listen • **Grade 2/Unit 6** **325**

Look for vowel teams such as *oi, ea, ee, oa, au, ai,* and *ou*
to help you read longer words with more than one syllable.

**A. Put the two syllables together to make a word. Write
the word on the line.**

1. point er _____

2. meat ball _____

3. moun tain _____

4. au tumn _____

5. fif teen _____

6. soap suds _____

7. out side _____

**B. Complete each sentence with a word you made.
Write the correct word on the line.**

8. Another word for the fall season is _____.

9. My brother is nine and my sister is _____.

10. My teacher used the _____ to show us places on
the map.

11. You need lots of _____ when you wash a car.

12. Have you ever eaten a _____ sandwich?

13. Last weekend, we hiked to the top of a _____.

14. Let's go _____ and ride our bikes.

© Macmillan/McGraw-Hill

CA R 1.3 Decode two-syllable nonsense words and regular
multisyllable words.

Name _____

Choose words from the box to finish the animal reports. Write the words on the lines.

| itches | puddles | handy | preen | beasts | nibble |

Bears

Bears are _____ because they have four feet. They

are gentle and _____ on berries. Bears rub their

backs against trees to scratch their _____.

Birds

Birds have beaks that are _____ for picking

up food. They also use their beaks to _____ or

smooth their feathers. Birds take baths in _____.

© Macmillan/McGraw-Hill

R 1.0 Word Analysis, Fluency, and Systematic Vocabulary Development

Splish! Splash! Animal Baths
Grade 2/Unit 6
327

- The words **a** and **an** are special adjectives called articles.
- Use the article **an** before a word that begins with a vowel sound.

    I want to hear <u>an</u> animal tale.

Circle the correct article *a* or *an* to complete each sentence. Write the article on the line.

1. Have you heard the story about

   (a, an) ant named Azizi? _____

2. Azizi is (a, an) African name. _____

3. Azizi is (a, an) friendly ant. _____

4. He has (a, an) lot of friends. _____

5. One of Azizi's friends is (a, an) elephant. _____

6. He is also friendly with (a, an) kangaroo. _____

7. It is (a, an) interesting story. _____

8. What (a, an) great ending! _____

© Macmillan/McGraw-Hill

CA LC 1.0 Written and Oral English Language Conventions

Name _____

Look for vowel teams such as *oi, ea, ee, oa, au, ai, ay,* and *ou* to help you read longer words with more than one syllable.

Choose the words from the word box that have the same vowel team as each of the words below. Write the words on the line.

feather	laundry	mountain	ahead	avoid	weekly
staircase	crayon	throat	contain	poison	agree
player	amount	caution	floating		

1. ready _____   _____

2. loud _____   _____

3. boat _____   _____

4. seem _____   _____

5. cause _____   _____

6. coin _____   _____

7. chain _____   _____

8. tray _____   _____

© Macmillan/McGraw-Hill

R 1.3 Decode two-syllable nonsense words and regular multisyllable words.

Splish! Splash! Animal Baths
Grade 2/Unit 6

329

way	ball	play	joy	explain
away	balloon	display	enjoy	meadow

A. Look at the spelling words in the box. Match each word to a vowel team syllable below. Write the spelling words on the lines.

ay syllable

I. _____

2. _____

3. _____

4. _____

oo syllable

5. _____

ai syllable

6. _____

ea syllable

7. _____

oy syllable

8. _____

9. _____

B. Write the spelling words that rhyme with each word.

10. contain

_____

II. stay

_____

_____

12. below

_____

13. moon

_____

14. toy

_____

15. stall

_____

© Macmillan/McGraw-Hill

CA **LC 1.8** Spell basic short-vowel, long-vowel, *r*-controlled, and consonant-blend patterns correctly.

Name _____

As you read *Splish! Splash! Animal Baths*, fill in the Compare and Contrast Chart.

Animal	Animal	Animal
Behavior	**Behavior**	**Behavior**

How does the information you wrote in this Compare and Contrast Chart help you to better understand *Splish! Splash! Animal Baths*?

R 2.0 Reading Comprehension

Splish! Splash! Animal Baths
Grade 2/Unit 6

331

© Macmillan/McGraw-Hill

Name _____

When you **compare**, you tell how things are alike.

When you **contrast**, you tell how things are different.

A. Put a check in each box if it tells something about bears or about pigs. Then use the chart to talk about how bears and pigs are alike and different.

	bear	pig
lives on a farm		
is a mammal		
has a snout		
has fur		
has two small eyes		

B. Write a sentence comparing a bear and a pig.
   Then write a sentence contrasting a bear and a pig.

_____

_____

_____

© Macmillan/McGraw-Hill

CA   R 2.0 Reading Comprehension

Practice

Vocabulary Strategy:
Word Parts:
Endings: *-s*, *-es*

Name _____

You can tell whether a noun is singular or plural by looking at its **ending**. Nouns that end with **-s** or **-es** are plural.

Read the story. Find the plural nouns. Write them on the lines. Then circle the ending in each noun you wrote.

We saw many animals on Mr. Brown's farm. There were horses in the field and pigs rolling in the mud. The ducks were near the lake, and the hens were in the barn. I liked the baby chicks. Mrs. Brown made lunches for us to eat. We sat on the benches and ate them.

I. _____   2. _____

3. _____   4. _____

5. _____   6. _____

7. _____   8. _____

© Macmillan/McGraw-Hill

CA **R 1.0** Word Analysis, Fluency, and Systematic Vocabulary Development

Splish! Splash! Animal Baths
Grade 2/Unit 6   **333**

As I read, I will pay attention to phrasing.

	Giraffes are the tallest animals on Earth. They are
9	mammals. This means they have warm blood and hair
18	on their bodies. They feed their babies milk.
26	Giraffes look a bit like jigsaw puzzles. They are
35	tan–colored with brown patches. They have long legs, long
44	necks, and tiny horns. Giraffes live for 20 to 30 years.
53	Most giraffes live on the African savanna. This is a dry
64	grassland with few trees.
68	Giraffes share their home with many other animals.
76	Lions also live on the savanna. Sometimes they
84	hunt giraffes.
86	Tick birds live on the savanna. They are handy because
96	they eat insects that live in the giraffes' fur. This helps the
108	giraffes have fewer **itches** caused by insects. 115

Comprehension Check

1. What do lions and giraffes have in common? **Compare and Contrast**

2. How do you know giraffes are the tallest animals on the African savanna? **Make and Confirm Predictions**

	Words Read	–	Number of Errors	=	Words Correct Score
First Read		–		=	
Second Read		–		=	

© Macmillan/McGraw-Hill

CA R 1.6 Read aloud fluently and accurately and with appropriate intonation and expression.

The **setting** is where or when a story or play happens.

Characters are people or animals in a story or play.

Read the play. Then answer the questions.

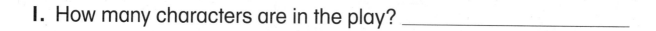

Happy Birthday, Duck!

(in the forest, on a sunny morning)

Bear: Hi, Rabbit, what are you doing?

Rabbit: *(holding a cake)* Hi, Bear. I am waiting
for Bird. We are going to visit Duck. Today
is Duck's birthday. Would you like to come
with us?

Bear: Sure. *(Bird walks into the forest.)*

Bear and Rabbit: Hi, Bird. Let's go to the lake
to surprise Duck. *(The three walk to the lake.)*

Bear, Rabbit, and Bird: Good Morning, Duck. Happy Birthday!

Duck: Thank you! What a wonderful surprise!

1. How many characters are in the play? _____

2. Where is the play set? _____

3. When does the play happen? _____

4. What is Rabbit holding? _____

© Macmillan/McGraw-Hill

CA R 2.0 Reading Comprehension

Splish! Splash! Animal Baths
Grade 2/Unit 6

335

- Use the article **a** before a word that begins with a consonant sound.
- Use the article **an** before a word that begins with a vowel sound.
- Remember to capitalize proper nouns.
- Capitalize a person's title. If it is an abbreviation, end it with a period.

Find the mistakes. Rewrite the paragraph correctly on the lines.

ms campbell read us a story about a old lady who swallows an fly. She also swallows an bird, an goat, and even an horse! I think the old lady should have gone to see dr doolittle. He's a animal doctor!

_____

_____

_____

_____

_____

CA LC 1.0 Written and Oral English Language Conventions

© Macmillan/McGraw-Hill

Name _____

A. There are five spelling mistakes in the report below. Circle the misspelled words. Write the words correctly on the lines below.

Do you enjoi walking in a medow? I do, and I will explayn why. I like to look at the plants and flowers. The beautiful flowers bring me joi on a gloomy day. I also like to look for animals. Sometimes I see rabbits running around. I think the rabbits like to playe chase!

1. _____

2. _____

3. _____

4. _____

5. _____

B. Writing

Write a short report about a plant or animal that lives near your home. Use four words from your spelling list. Circle the spelling words you use.

_____

_____

_____

_____

_____

© Macmillan/McGraw-Hill

LC 1.8 Spell basic short-vowel, long-vowel, r-controlled, and consonant-blend patterns correctly.

Words with **vowel consonant *e* syllables** often have the long vowel sound. Look for final *e* syllables such as *a* consonant *e*, *u* consonant *e*, *o* consonant *e*, *e* consonant *e*, and *i* consonant *e* to help you read longer words.

A. Underline the vowel consonant *e* syllable in each of these words.

I. relate

2. compete

3. excite

4. reside

B. Divide each word into syllables. Then write each syllable.

5. arrive

_____ _____

6. vibrate

_____ _____

7. racetrack

_____ _____

8. hopeful

_____ _____

CA **R 1.3** Decode two-syllable nonsense words and regular multisyllable words.

© Macmillan/McGraw-Hill

Name _____

Use a word from the box to complete each clue. Then write your answers in the puzzle.

| hardest | conservation | extinct | trouble | remains |

Across

2. _____ are what is left of an animal's body after it has died.

3. An animal that is _____ has died out forever.

5. You would have less _____ if you followed directions.

Down

1. Using as little water as you can is good _____.

4. Diamonds are the _____ kind of stone.

Name _____

- **Antonyms** are words with opposite meanings.
- **Synonyms** are words with the same or almost the same meanings.

| big | slow | nice | huge | happy | funny |

Write an antonym for the underlined word. Choose a word from the box.

1. We read a <u>sad</u> folk tale. _____

2. The tale is about a <u>tiny</u> frog named Ling. _____

3. Ling was a <u>fast</u> hopper. _____

Write a synonym for the underlined word. Choose a word from the box.

4. Ling had <u>silly</u> friends. _____

5. One of Ling's friends was a <u>large</u> mouse. _____

6. She was a very <u>friendly</u> mouse. _____

© Macmillan/McGraw-Hill

CA **LC 1.0** Written and Oral English Language Conventions

Vowel consonant *e* syllables often have the long sound of the vowel.

Draw a line to divide each word into syllables. Then complete each sentence below with the correct word.

1. awoke

2. spaceship

3. athlete

4. locate

5. divide

6. Please help me _____ our state on the map.

7. Let's _____ the pizza in half to share.

8. My dog _____ when she heard the crash of thunder.

9. I'd like to travel to the moon in a _____.

10. The _____ who won the race ran very fast.

© Macmillan/McGraw-Hill

CA **R 1.3** Decode two-syllable nonsense words and regular multisyllable words.

A Way to Help Planet Earth   341
Grade 2/Unit 6

Practice

Spelling: Final e Syllables

Name _____

| place | nine | side | face | these |
| replace | ninety | sidewalk | inside | tadpole |

A. Word Sort

Look at the spelling words in the box. Match each word to the long vowel sound in its final e syllable. Write the spelling words on the lines below.

long a
1. _____
2. _____
3. _____

long e
4. _____

long i
5. _____
6. _____
7. _____
8. _____
9. _____

long o
10. _____

B. Missing Letter

The vowel is missing from each spelling word below. Write the missing letter in the box. Then write the spelling word correctly on the line.

11. repl ☐ ce _____
12. th ☐ se _____
13. ins ☐ de _____
14. n ☐ nety _____
15. tadp ☐ le _____

© Macmillan/McGraw-Hill

342 A Way to Help Planet Earth
Grade 2/Unit 6

CA LC 1.8 Spell basic short-vowel, long-vowel, r-controlled, and consonant-blend patterns correctly.

Name _____

As you read *A Way to Help Planet Earth*, fill in the Problem and Solution Chart.

Problem

⬇

Steps to Solution

⬇

Solution

How does the Problem and Solution Chart help you understand
A Way to Help Planet Earth?

© Macmillan/McGraw-Hill

In most stories, the main character has a **problem**. The **solution** is how the character solves the problem.

A. Each set of sentences tells about a problem and a solution. Write the letter _P_ next to the sentence that tells the problem. Write the letter _S_ next to the sentence that tells the solution.

I. There was a lot of trash around our school. ____

Different classes take turns cleaning up the schoolyard. ____

2. Now we turn off lights when we leave a room. ____

We were using too much energy in our house. ____

3. People started walking and riding bikes instead of driving. ____

The air in our city was dirty because of pollution from cars. ____

4. Some animals are becoming extinct, or dying out. ____

People in the government are passing laws to protect animals. ____

B. Write a solution for this problem.

5. Balloons can hurt birds and other animals who try to eat them.

_____

© Macmillan/McGraw-Hill

CA R 2.0 Reading Comprehension

Multiple-meaning words are words that have more than one meaning.

Use the dictionary entry to figure out which meaning is used in each sentence. Write the number of the meaning that matches its use in the sentence.

bank *noun* **1.** object or place for keeping money. *I have a **bank** that is shaped like a pig.* **2.** the land along the sides of a river. *Tall grasses grow along the **bank**.* *verb* **3.** to cover a fire with ashes so that it burns slower. *When you **bank** a fire, it gets less air.*

1. A duck and her ducklings are walking along the **bank**. _____

2. **Bank** the fire before the flames get too high. _____

3. I have 20 quarters in my **bank**. _____

4. When we're camping, we **bank** the fire after dinner. _____

5. Does your **bank** lock with a key? _____

6. Let's sit on the **bank** and put our feet in the river. _____

© Macmillan/McGraw-Hill

Name _____

As I read, I will pay attention to the pronunciation of vocabulary words.

	Sometimes there is an oil spill. This may happen
9	because the tanker has an accident. Or the tanker may
19	be caught in a natural disaster, such as a hurricane.
29	In an oil spill, most of the oil floats on the water.
41	It spreads very quickly. It forms a layer called an oil
52	slick. The more the oil spreads, the thinner the layer
62	becomes.
63	Then winds and ocean waves carry the oil toward
72	the shore. The oil covers the rocks and sand on the
83	beach.
84	Even a small spill means big **trouble**. It can kill
94	hundreds of animals. A large spill can kill thousands!
103	When oil spills happen, endangered animals are at
111	risk of becoming **extinct**. 115

Comprehension Check

1. What happens when a tanker has an oil spill? **Problem and Solution**

2. How can a large oil spill cause animals to become extinct? **Cause and Effect**

	Words Read	−	Number of Errors	=	Words Correct Score
First Read		−		=	
Second Read		−		=	

© Macmillan/McGraw-Hill

R 1.6 Read aloud fluently and accurately and with appropriate intonation and expression.

You can use **text features** and **changes in print** to get information. A **caption** is a short label that tells about a picture. A **sidebar** can be a shorter story, a chart or graph, or a picture that is placed next to the main article. **Bold type** is heavy, dark type. *Italic type* slants to the right. Authors use these features to call attention to important words.

Read the article below. Then answer the questions.

How Can We Care for the Land?
Planting trees can help care for the land.
Recycling paper, glass, cans, and plastic can help care for the land.
More ways to help care for the land can be found in the book *What I Can Do to Help*.

planting trees

recycling

I. Underline the title of this article.

2. How is the title different from the rest of the text? _____

_____

3. Draw a box around the words below the title that the author wants to call special attention to.

4. What kind of information is in the sidebar? _____

_____

© Macmillan/McGraw-Hill

Name _____

Problem/Solution Writing Frame

Summarize *A Way to Help Planet Earth*.
Use the Problem/Solution Writing Frame below.

One of Earth's biggest **problems** is trash. Trash comes from _____

_____

_____

_____

_____.

To **solve** this problem, _____

_____

_____

_____

_____.

To recycle, people _____

_____

_____

_____

_____.

Recycling is one way to make a big difference in solving our planet's trash
problem.

Rewrite the completed summary on another sheet of paper. Keep it as a model
for writing a summary of an article or selection using this text structure.

© Macmillan/McGraw-Hill

CA **R 2.0** Reading Comprehension

Name _____

- Begin every sentence with a capital letter.
- End statements and commands with a period.
- End a question with a question mark.
- End an exclamation with an exclamation mark.
- A proper noun begins with a capital letter.

Find the mistakes. Rewrite the paragraph correctly on the lines.

a new boy joined our class today his name is oren. do you know where Oren is from. he moved here all the way from Israel? "Please welcome Oren," said our teacher

_____

_____

_____

_____

_____

© Macmillan/McGraw-Hill

Name _____

A. There are five spelling mistakes in the paragraph below. Circle the misspelled words. Write the words correctly on the lines below.

Our new city park is a very special plase. It used to be old and dirty, but people in our neighborhood decided to clean it up. First, they raised money to replaice the broken slide. Then they built a huge swing set. It has nyne swings! They also put in a new sidwalk so we could ride our bikes around the park. I'm so glad theese people are my neighbors. They really work hard to make our city better!

I. _____   2. _____   3. _____

4. _____   5. _____

B. Writing

Write a paragraph about something in your school or neighborhood you would like to make better. Use four words from your spelling list.

_____

_____

_____

_____

_____

CA **LC 1.8** Spell basic short-vowel, long-vowel, *r*-controlled, and consonant-blend patterns correctly.

© Macmillan/McGraw-Hill

Name _____

When two vowels together stand for one sound, both vowels appear in the same syllable. The syllable is a **vowel team syllable**.

A. Draw a line to divide each word into syllables. Then match the word to the picture it names.

1. steamship

2. raccoon

3. suitcase

4. elbow

B. Divide each word into syllables. Then write each syllable.

5. mailing _____ _____

6. coastline _____ _____

© Macmillan/McGraw-Hill

CA R 1.3 Decode two-syllable nonsense words and regular multisyllable words.

Super Storms • **Grade 2/Unit 6** 351

A. Write the correct word from the box next to each definition.

> beware   destroy   grasslands   prevent   uprooted   violent

1. to keep something from happening: ___ ___ ___ ___ ___ ___ ___
                                              11   4

2. pulled up by the roots: ___ ___ ___ ___ ___ ___ ___ ___
                               3   10   9

3. to ruin completely: ___ ___ ___ ___ ___ ___ ___
                           5   8

4. lands covered with grass, where animals feed:

   ___ ___ ___ ___ ___ ___ ___ ___ ___ ___
       7

5. happening with or because of a strong force:

   ___ ___ ___ ___ ___ ___ ___
               1

6. to be on one's guard: ___ ___ ___ ___ ___ ___
                                              6

B. Write the numbered letters from your answers on the lines below to find the answer to the riddle.

   Beware of me! I can be **violent**, **destroy** buildings, **uproot** trees, and damage **grasslands**. What am I?

       H   M
   ___ ___ ___ ___ ___ ___ ___ ___ ___ ___ ___ ___
    1   2   3   4   5   6   7   8   9 10 11 12

© Macmillan/McGraw-Hill

CA R 1.0 Word Analysis, Fluency, and Systematic Vocabulary Development

Name _____

- You can use **adjectives to compare** people, places, or things.
- Add **-est** to an adjective to compare more than two nouns.

    Cymbals are the <u>loudest</u> instruments of all.

Look at the pictures and read the sentence. Write an adjective that ends with -est on the line.

1. The harp is the _____ instrument.

2. The square is the _____ shape.

3. Hannah is the _____ jumper.

4. Evan is the _____ runner.

5. Jenny is the _____ child.

© Macmillan/McGraw-Hill

When two vowels together stand for one sound, both vowels appear in the same syllable. The syllable is a **vowel team syllable**.

Choose the words from the word box that have the same vowel team as each of the words below. Write the words and divide them into syllables.

weaken	window	maybe	hooded	untrue	enjoy
Monday	handbook	royal	peanut	bluebird	blowing

1. glue _____ _____

2. snow _____ _____

3. treat _____ _____

4. took _____ _____

5. clay _____ _____

6. boy _____ _____

© Macmillan/McGraw-Hill

CA R 1.3 Decode two-syllable nonsense words and regular multisyllable word

Name _____

| be | reaches | highway | between | reach |
| wood | root | wooden | way | uprooted |

A. Word Sort

Look at the spelling words in the box. Write the spelling words that have one syllable.

I. _____   2. _____   3. _____

4. _____   5. _____

Write the spelling words that have two syllables.

6. _____   7. _____

8. _____   9. _____

Write the spelling word that has three syllables.

10. _____

B. Find the Pattern

Read each group of words. Circle the word that does not have the same vowel team.

II. wood, way, wooden

12. highway, wood, way

13. reaches, between, reach

14. root, reach, uprooted

© Macmillan/McGraw-Hill

LC 1.8 Spell basic short-vowel, long-vowel, r-controlled, and consonant-blend patterns correctly.

Super Storms • Grade 2/Unit 6   355

As you read *Super Storms*, fill in the Cause and
Effect Chart.

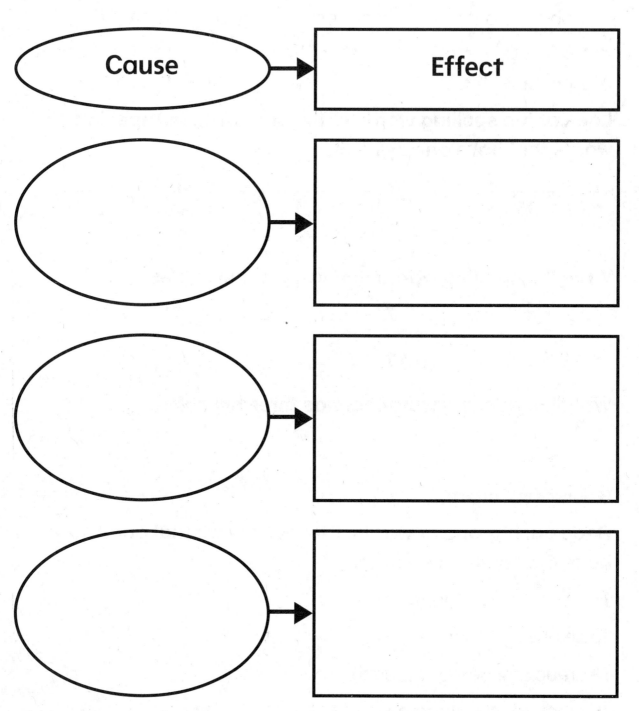

How does the information you wrote in this Cause and Effect Chart
help you to better understand *Super Storms*?

 R 2.6 Recognize cause-and-effect relationships in a text.

© Macmillan/McGraw-Hill

> A **cause** is what makes something happen.
> The **effect** is what happens.

Write a cause or an effect for each item.

1. Cause: _____

Effect: Our snowman melted.

2. Cause: I drove over a nail on my bike.

Effect: _____

3. Cause: _____

Effect: This morning, there was a huge puddle in the street.

4. Cause: Lightning hit a big tree.

Effect: _____

© Macmillan/McGraw-Hill

CA R 2.6 Recognize cause-and-effect relationships in a text.

Super Storms • Grade 2/Unit 6   **357**

Name _____

A **compound word** is a word that is made up of two smaller words. You can often figure out the meaning of a compound word by thinking about the meanings of the smaller words.

rain + coat = raincoat   snow + suit = snowsuit

Read each sentence. Circle the compound word. Then write its meaning on the line.

1. Big, fluffy snowflakes fell during the blizzard yesterday.

_____

2. The strong wind made the sailboats speed across the water.

_____

3. The storm made the power go out, so we ate dinner by candlelight.

_____

4. The heavy rain and loud thunder make thunderstorms scary.

_____

5. Be sure to wipe your muddy shoes on the doormat.

_____

© Macmillan/McGraw-Hill

CA R 1.8 Use knowledge of individual words in unknown compound words to predict their meaning.

As I read, I will pay attention to phrasing.

	Suddenly, Abby felt the air get cooler. She stood up and looked
12	at the sea. Abby saw big black clouds moving in the sky.
24	"Better **beware**! A great big storm is coming this way!"
34	Abby cried out.
37	Then the wind blew in. A **violent** gust took them all by
49	surprise! They couldn't **prevent** their towels from flying up in
59	the air. Wild weather was on its way. Fudge ran around in circles.
72	As the family packed up the picnic, sand blew in their faces.
84	Waves were quickly rolling onto the beach.
91	Lightning flashed over the sea. Thunder rumbled, closer and
100	closer.
101	"Look!" shouted Jack. "The tree is being **uprooted** by the
111	storm!" 112

Comprehension Check

1. How did Abby know a big storm was coming? **Make and Confirm Predictions**

2. What caused the towels to fly up in the air? **Cause and Effect**

	Words Read	−	Number of Errors	=	Words Correct Score
First Read		−		=	
Second Read		−		=	

© Macmillan/McGraw-Hill

CA R 1.6 Read aloud fluently and accurately and with appropriate intonation and expression.

Super Storms • Grade 2/Unit 6   359

Repetition is when one word or phrase appears two or more times in a poem.

Word choice is important in a poem. The words a poet chooses give the poem a certain feeling or mood.

Read the nursery rhyme. Then answer the questions below.

Three little kittens lost their mittens,
And they began to cry,
Oh, mother dear, we sadly fear,
Our mittens we have lost.

Lost your mittens! You naughty kittens!
Then you shall have no pie.
Meow, meow! Meow, meow!
Then you shall have no pie.

1. What words are repeated in this rhyme? _____

_____

2. What is the mood in the first verse? _____

3. Which words or lines help create the mood of the first verse?

_____

4. What is the mood in the second verse? _____

5. Which words or lines help create the mood of the second verse?

_____

© Macmillan/McGraw-Hill

 R 2.0 Reading Comprehension

Name _____

- Add *-er* to an adjective to compare two nouns.
- Add *-est* to an adjective to compare more than two nouns.
- Add an apostrophe and *s* to make a singular noun possessive.
- Add an apostrophe to make most plural nouns possessive.

Underline the correct adjective to complete each sentence. Add an apostrophe to each possessive noun. Write the sentence correctly on the line.

1. Tims painting is the (bigger, biggest) of the five.

_____

2. Is Mayas painting (smaller, smallest) than Enricos painting?

_____

3. The three boys easels are the (neater, neatest) in the class.

_____

4. The second-graders paintbrushes are (thicker, thickest) than the third-graders brushes.

_____

_____

5. The teachers paintbrush is the (thinner, thinnest).

_____

© Macmillan/McGraw-Hill

A. There are six spelling mistakes in the report below. Circle the misspelled words. Write the words correctly on the lines below.

Last night, there was a bad thunderstorm. A tornado came through and uproted a tree. The tree fell on the highwa. Now the tree reches across the road. There are pieces of wod all over. People will not bea able to drive on the road. They will need to find another wae to get places.

1. _____   2. _____   3. _____

4. _____   5. _____   6. _____

B. Writing

Write a short report about something that happened after a storm. Use four of the spelling words in your report.

_____

_____

_____

_____

_____

_____

© Macmillan/McGraw-Hill

CA **LC 1.8** Spell basic short-vowel, long-vowel, r-controlled, and consonant-blend patterns correctly.

Name _____

When an *r*-controlled vowel appears in a word, the vowel and the letter **r** stay in the same syllable. This syllable is an **r-controlled syllable**.

A. Put the two syllables together to make a word. Write it on the line.

I. tur tle _____

2. car pet _____

3. squir rel _____

4. pep per _____

B. Use a word that you made to answer each riddle. Write the word on the line.

5. I lie on the floor. What am I? _____

6. I can make you sneeze. What am I? _____

7. I hardly ever win a race. What am I? _____

8. I have a bushy tail. What am I? _____

© Macmillan/McGraw-Hill

R 1.3 Decode two-syllable nonsense words and regular multisyllable words.

Pushing Up the Sky • **Grade 2/Unit 6** **363**

Name _____

A. Choose the word from the box that best matches each meaning below. Write the word on the line.

| jabbing | agreed | randomly | signal | gathered |

I. understood or had the same idea _____

2. a sign or warning _____

3. fast, sharp pushing _____

4. brought together _____

5. with no clear pattern _____

B. Write three sentences with words from the box.

6. _____

_____

7. _____

_____

8. _____

_____

CA R 1.0 Word Analysis, Fluency, and Systematic Vocabulary Development

© Macmillan/McGraw-Hill

Name _____

- An **adverb** tells more about a verb.
- An adverb can tell when or where.
  An inventor visited our class <u>yesterday</u>. (when)
  She sat <u>nearby</u>. (where)

Circle the adverb in each sentence. On the lines, write the word *when* if it tells when. Write *where* if it tells where.

1. Long ago, George Washington Carver invented many uses for

peanuts. _____

2. The peanuts grew outside. _____

3. Do you think Mr. Carver lived nearby? _____

4. Mr. Carver never sold his inventions. _____

5. Finally, Mr. Carver won a medal for his work. _____

6. Which of Mr. Carver's inventions do you use today?

_____

© Macmillan/McGraw-Hill

When an *r*-controlled vowel appears in a word, the vowel and the letter **r** stay in the same syllable.

Choose the words from the word box that have the same *r*-controlled vowel as each of the words below. Write the words and divide them into syllables.

birthday	prepare	curtain	father	stirring	orbit
harvest	sharpen	waiter	report	murmur	careless

1. march _____ _____

2. cord _____ _____

3. hurt _____ _____

4. share _____ _____

5. sister _____ _____

6. first _____ _____

CA **R 1.3** Decode two-syllable nonsense words and regular multisyllable words.

© Macmillan/McGraw-Hill

Name _____

jump	high	star	other	ever
jumper	higher	starry	mother	paper

A. Word Sort

Look at the spelling words in the box. Write the spelling words that have one syllable. Then write the words that have two syllables.

one syllable

1. _____

2. _____

3. _____

two syllables

4. _____

5. _____

6. _____

7. _____

8. _____

9. _____

10. _____

B. Rhyme Time

Write the spelling word that rhymes with each of these words.

11. flier

_____

12. vapor

_____

13. never

_____

14. bumper

_____

© Macmillan/McGraw-Hill

LC 1.8 Spell basic short-vowel, long-vowel, *r*-controlled, and consonant-blend patterns correctly.

CA

Pushing Up the Sky • Grade 2/Unit 6   **367**

Name _____

As you read *Pushing Up the Sky*, fill in the Problem and Solution Chart.

Problem

↓

Steps to Solution

↓

Solution

How does the information you wrote in this Problem and Solution Chart help you to better understand *Pushing Up the Sky*?

© Macmillan/McGraw-Hill

R 2.0 Reading Comprehension

Name _____

In most stories, the main character has a **problem**. The **solution** is how the character solves the problem.

A. Each set of sentences tells about a problem and a solution. Write the letter _P_ next to the sentence that tells the problem. Write the letter _S_ next to the sentence that tells the solution.

1. It was cold on the stage. ____

   The teacher turned on the heat. ____

2. The teacher asked more children to try out for the play. ____

   There were not enough children for all the parts in the play. ____

3. The teacher turned on the lights. ____

   The stage was too dark. ____

4. I didn't have the right clothes to wear in the play. ____

   I borrowed clothes from a friend. ____

B. Write a solution for this problem.

5. We hadn't sold enough tickets for the play.

_____

© Macmillan/McGraw-Hill

You can add **endings** to a **base word** to make new words. The endings can change the meaning of the base word.

A. Read each word. Circle the base word. Draw a line under the ending. Then write the word in a sentence on the line.

1. helped

_____

2. fixing

_____

3. wanted

_____

B. Add the ending to the base word to make a new word. Write the word on the line. Then write the new word in a sentence.

4. go + ing = _____

_____

5. cook + ed = _____

_____

© Macmillan/McGraw-Hill

CA **R 1.0** Word Analysis, Fluency, and Systematic Vocabulary Development

Name _____

As I read, I will pay attention to expression.

14	**Narrator:** This is a play based on a folk tale from Nigeria. A long time ago, the Sky was very close to Earth. Whenever people were
26	hungry, they reached up **randomly** and broke off a piece of the Sky.
39	**Villager 1:** Mmm, tastes like corn.
44	**Villager 2:** Mmm, tastes like roasted potatoes.
50	**Villager 3:** Mmm, tastes like pineapple.
55	**Narrator:** The Sky tasted different to everyone. But all the
65	people agreed it was delicious.
70	**Narrator:** The people never had to work for food. They spent their
82	time making beautiful art, telling stories, and having festivals.
91	**Villager 1:** How many guests will King Oba invite to the
101	next festival?
103	**Villager 2:** 40!
104	**Villager 3:** 80!
105	**Child 1:** 100! 100!
106	**Narrator:** At festival time, King Oba's servants made feasts from
116	pieces of the Sky. 120

Comprehension Check

1. What did people do when they were hungry? **Problem and Solution**

2. According to the folk tale, how was the world different a long time ago? **Main Idea and Details**

	Words Read	–	Number of Errors	=	Words Correct Score
First Read		–		=	
Second Read		–		=	

© Macmillan/McGraw-Hill

R 1.6 Read aloud fluently and accurately and with appropriate intonation and **expression**.

CA

An **interview** is a group of questions asked by one person and answered by another.

Read this short interview with actress Roberta Camsen. Then answer the questions below.

Question: Roberta, when did you decide that you wanted to be an actor?

Answer: I was in all the school plays when I was young. That is how I found out that I love to act. Then I went to college and took classes in theater and acting.

Question: How did you get started as an actor?

Answer: I moved to New York because there are so many plays performed there. I got a few small parts in plays and in television commercials. It was really hard for a while. But I kept at it. Gradually the parts got bigger. People got to know me.

I. What is one fact you learned from this interview?

_____

_____

2. Underline two sentences from the interview that tell how Roberta feels.

3. Write another question you could ask Roberta Camsen in this

interview. _____

_____

© Macmillan/McGraw-Hill

CA **R 2.1** Use titles, tables of contents, and chapter headings to locate information in expository text.

- The pronoun *I* is always a capital letter.
- A proper noun begins with a capital letter.
- Add an apostrophe and *-s* to make a singular noun possessive.

Find the mistakes. Rewrite the paragraph correctly on the lines.

garrett morgan was an inventor from cleveland who worked to make peoples lives safer. morgans invention of the traffic signal made traveling safer. morgans' gas mask also kept people safe. i hope to create a life-saving invention one day.

_____

_____

_____

_____

_____

_____

© Macmillan/McGraw-Hill

A. There are six spelling mistakes in the paragraph below. Circle the misspelled words. Write the words correctly on the lines below.

Why do we have stary skies? My mother made up this story and wrote it down on papir. Once the stars lived on Earth, but they were too hot. People had to jump over them. Many people tried to think of othur places for stars to live. A very tall man had an idea. He was a great jumpur. He jumped up high and put the stars in the sky. Then he moved them even highr. Ever since, the stars have lived there. Sometimes, though, you might see a starr fall. Maybe it misses its old home.

I. _____   2. _____   3. _____

4. _____   5. _____   6. _____

B. Writing

Write a story about something else in nature. Use four words from your spelling list.

_____

_____

_____

_____

_____

_____

© Macmillan/McGraw-Hill

CA **LC 1.8** Spell basic short-vowel, long-vowel, *r*-controlled, and consonant-blend patterns correctly.